D1316518

BIRDS IN LEGEND
FABLE AND FOLKLORE

ST. FRANCIS PREACHING TO THE BIRDS.

Attributed to Giotto

BIRDS IN LEGEND
FABLE AND FOLKLORE

BY

ERNEST INGERSOLL

AUTHOR OF "THE LIFE OF MAMMALS," "NATURE'S CALENDAR,"
"THE WIT OF THE WILD," ETC.: AND SECRETARY
OF THE AUTHORS CLUB, NEW YORK

NEW YORK

LONGMANS, GREEN AND CO.
1923

Now Reissued by
Singing Tree Press
1400 Book Tower, Detroit, Michigan 1968

CONTENTS

BIRDS IN LEGEND
FABLE AND FOLKLORE

BIRDS IN LEGEND
FABLE AND FOLKLORE

I

A CHAT WITH THE INTENDING READER

Angus Mac-ind-oc was the Cupid of the Gaels. He was a harper of the sweetest music, and was attended by birds, his own transformed kisses, which hovered, invisible, over young men and maidens of Erin, whispering love into their ears.

WHEN we say, "A little bird told me," we are talking legend and folklore and superstition all at once. There is an old Basque story of a bird —always a small one in these tales—that tells the truth; and our Biloxi Indians used to say the same of the hummingbird. Breton peasants still credit all birds with the power of using human language on proper occasions, and traditions in all parts of the world agree that every bird had this power once on a time if not now. The fireside-tales of the nomads of Oriental deserts or of North American plains and forest alike attest faith in this power; and conversation by and with birds is almost the main stock of the stories heard on our Southern cotton-plantations. You will perhaps recall the bulbul bazar of the *Arabian Nights,* and, if you please, you may read in another chapter of the conversational pewit and hoopoe of Solomonic fame.

Biblical authority exists in the confidence of the

Prophet Elijah that a "bird of the air . . . shall tell the matter"; and monkish traditions abound in revelations whispered in the ear of the faithful by winged messengers from divine sources, as you may read further along if you have patience to turn the leaves. The poets keep alive the pretty fiction; and the rest of us resort to the phrase with an arch smile whenever we do not care to quote our authority for repeating some half-secret bit of gossip. "This magical power of understanding bird-talk," says Halliday,[1] * "is regularly the way in which the seers of myths obtain their information."

Primitive men—and those we style the Ancients were primitive so far as nature is concerned—regarded birds as supernaturally wise. This canniness is implied in many of the narratives and incidents set down in the succeeding pages; and in view of it birds came to be regarded by early man with great respect, yet also with apprehension, for they might utilize their knowledge to his harm. For example: The Canada jay is believed by the Indians along the northern shore of Hudson Bay to give warning whenever they approach an Eskimo camp —usually, of course, with hostile intent; and naturally those Indians kill that kind of jay whenever they can.

The ability in birds to speak implies knowledge, and Martha Young[2] gives us a view of this logic prevailing among the old-time southern darkies:

---

* This and similar "superior" figures throughout the text refer to the List of Books in the Appendix, where the author and title of the publication alluded to will be found under its number.

The author takes this opportunity, in place of a perfunctory Preface, to make grateful acknowledgment of assistance to Professor A. V. H. JACKSON, who revised the chapter on fabulous birds; to Mr. STEWART CULIN, helpful in Chinese matters, etc.; to Professor JUSTIN H. SMITH, who scanned the whole manuscript; and to others who furnished valuable facts and suggestions.

Sis' Dove she know mo'n anybody or anything in de worl'.
She know pintedly de time anybody gwine die. You'll hear
her moanin' fer a passin' soul 'fo' you hear de bell tone.
She know 'fo' cotton-plantin' time whe'r de craps dat gatherin'
'll be good er bad. 'Fo' folks breaks up de new groun' er
bust out middles, Sis' Dove know what de yield 'll be. She
know it an' she'll tell it, too. 'Caze ev'ybody know if
Sis' Dove coo on de right han' of a man plowin', dare 'll be
a good crap dat year; but ef she coo on de lef' dar 'll be a
faillery crap dat year.
Sis' Dove she know about all de craps dat grow out er de
groun' but she 'special know about corn, fer she plant de fi'st
grain er corn dat ever was plant' in de whole worl'. Whar
she git it? . . . Umm—hum! You tell me dat!

From the belief in the intuitive wisdom of birds comes
the world-wide confidence in their prophetic power.
Hence their actions, often so mysterious, have been
watched with intense interest, and everything unusual
in their behavior was noticed in the hope that it might
express a revelation from on high. Advantage was taken
of this pathetic hope and assurance by the Roman augurs
in their legalized ornithomancy, of which some description will be found in another chapter. Nine-tenths of it
was priestly humbug to keep ordinary folks in mental
subjection, as priestcraft has ever sought to do. The
remaining tenth has become the basis of the present
popular faith in birds' ability to foretell coming weather.
Let me cite a few aboriginal examples of this faith,
more or less sincere, in the ability and willingness of
birds to warn inquiring humanity.

The Omahas and other Siouan Indians used to say
that when whippoorwills sing at night, saying "Hoia,
hohin?" one replies "No." If the birds stop at once, it is
a sign that the answerer will soon die, but if the birds
keep on calling he or she will live a long time. The
Utes of Colorado, however, declare that this bird is the

god of the night, and that it made the moon by magic, transforming a frog into it; while the Iroquois indulged in the pretty fancy that the moccasin-flowers (cypripediums) are whippoorwills' shoes.

This is a little astray from my present theme, to which we may return by quoting from Waterton [73] that if one of the related goatsuckers of the Amazon Valley be heard close to an Indian's or a negro's hut, from that night evil fortune sits brooding over it. In Costa Rica bones of whippoorwills are dried and ground to a fine powder by the Indians when they want to concoct a charm against some enemy; mixed with tobacco it will form a cigarette believed to cause certain death to the person smoking it.

To the mountaineers of the southern Alleghanies the whippoorwill reveals how long it will be before marriage —as many years as its notes are repeated: as I have heard the bird reiterate its cry more than 800 times without taking breath, this must often be a discouraging report to an anxious maid or bachelor. One often hears it said lightly in New England that a whippoorwill calling very near a house portends death, but I can get no evidence that this "sign" is really attended to anywhere in the northern United States.

This, and the equally nocturnal screechowl (against which the darkies have many "conjurings") are not the only birds feared by rural folk in the Southern States, especially in the mountains. A child in a family of Georgia "crackers" fell ill, and his mother gave this account of it to a sympathetic friend:

Mikey is bound to die. I've know'd it all along. All las' week the moanin' doves was comin' roun' the house, and this mornin' one come in at the window right by Mikey's head, an' cooed an' moaned. I couldn't scare it away, else a witch would 'a' put a spell on me.

Mikey lived to become a drunkard, is the unfeeling comment of the reporter of this touching incident in *The Journal of American Folklore.*

"One constantly hears by day the note of the limócon, a wood-pigeon which exercises a most extraordinary interest over the lives of many of the wild people, for they believe that the direction and nature of its notes augur good or ill for the enterprises they have in hand." This memorandum, in Dean Worcester's valuable book on the Philippines,[3] is apt to the purpose of this introductory chapter, leading me to say that the continuing reader will find doves (which are much the same in all parts of the world) conspicuous in legend, fable and ceremony; also that the "direction and nature" of their voices, as heard, is one of the most important elements in the consideration of birds in general as messengers and prophets—functions to which I shall often have occasion to refer, and on which are founded the ancient systems of bird-divination.

In these United States little superstition relating to animals has survived, partly because the wild creatures here were strange to the pioneers, who were poorly acquainted with their characteristics, but mainly because such fears and fancies were left in the Old World with other rubbish not worth the freight-charges; yet a few quaint notions came along, like small heirlooms of no particular value that folks dislike to throw away until they must. Almost all such mental keepsakes belong to people in the backward parts of the country, often with an ill-fitting application to local birds. A conspicuous disappearance is that venerable body of forebodings and fancies attached to the European cuckoo, totally unknown or disregarded here, because our American cuckoos have no such irregular habits as gave rise to the myths and superstitions clustering about that bird in Europe.

We saw a moment ago that the negro farmer estimated what the yield of his field would be by the direction from which the dove's message came to his ears. I have another note that if one hears the first mourning-dove of the year above him he will prosper: if from below him his own course henceforth will be down hill.

This matter of direction whence (and also of number) is of vital importance in interpreting bird-prophecy the world over, as will be fully shown in a subsequent chapter. Even in parts of New England it is counted "unlucky" to see two crows together flying toward the left—a plain borrowing from the magpie-lore of Old England. In the South it is thought that if two quails fly up in front of a man on the way to conclude a bargain he will do well to abandon the intended business. Break up a killdeer's nest and you will soon break a leg or arm —and so on.

There always have been persons who were much disturbed when a bird fluttered against a closed window. A rooster crowing into an open house-door foretells a visitor. The plantation darkies of our Southern States believe that when shy forest-birds come close about a dwelling as if frightened, or, wandering within it, beat their wings wildly in search of an exit, so some soul will flutteringly seek escape from that house—and "right soon." Similar fears afflict the timid on the other side of the globe. On the contrary, and more naturally, it is esteemed among us an excellent omen when wild birds nest fearlessly about a negro's or a mountaineer's cabin.

When a Georgia girl first hears in the spring the plaintive call of returning doves she must immediately attend to it if she is curious as to her future partner in life. She must at once take nine steps forward and nine backward, then take off her right shoe: in it she will discover a hair of the man she is to marry—but how to find its owner is not explained! This bit of rustic divination is plainly transferred from the old English formula toward the first-heard cuckoo, as may be learned from Gay's *The Sheperd's Week*,[8] which is a treasury of rustic customs in Britain long ago. Says one of the maids:

> Then doff'd my shoe, and by my troth I swear,
> Therein I spy'd this yellow, frizzled hair.

This matter of the hair is pure superstition allied to magic, in practicing which, indeed, birds have often been degraded to an evil service very remote from their nature. Thiselton Dyer quotes an Irish notion that "in everyone's head there is a particular hair which, if the swallow can pluck it, dooms the wretched individual to eternal perdition." A Baltimore folklorist warns every lady against letting birds build nests with the combings of her hair, as it will turn the unfortunate woman crazy. Any woman afraid of this should beware of that dear little sprite of our garden shrubbery, the chipping-sparrow, for it always lines its tiny nest with hair. This notion is another importation, for it has long been a saying in Europe that if a bird uses human hair in its nest the owner of the hair will have headaches and later baldness. Curiously enough the Seneca Indians, one of the five Iroquois tribes, are said to have long practised a means, as they believed it to be, of communicating with a maiden-relative, after her death, by capturing a fledgling bird with a noose made from her hair. The bird was kept caged until it began to sing, when it was liberated and was believed to carry to the knowledge of the departed one a whispered message of love.

Now the idea underlying all this faith in the supernatural wisdom and prophetic gift in birds is the general supposition that they are spirits, or, at any rate, possessed by spirits, a doctrine that appears in various guises but is universal in the world of primitive culture—a world nearer to us sophisticated readers than perhaps we realize: but a good many little children inhabit it, even within our doors.

"The primitive mind," as Dr. Brinton asserts, "did not recognize any deep distinction between the lower animals and man"; and continues:

The savage knew that the beast was his superior in many points, in craft and in strength, in fleetness and intuition, and he regarded it with respect. To him the brute had a soul not inferior to his own, and a language which the wise among men might on occasion learn. . . . Therefore with wide unanimity he placed certain species of animals nearer to God than is man himself, or even identified them with the manifestations of the Highest.

None was in this respect a greater favorite than the bird. Its soaring flight, its strange or sweet notes, the marked hues of its plumage, combined to render it a fit emblem of power and beauty. The Dyaks of Borneo trace their descent to Singalang Burong, the god of birds; and birds as the ancestors of the totemic family are extremely common among the American Indians. The Eskimos say that they have the faculty of soul or life beyond all other creatures, and in most primitive tribes they have been regarded as the messengers of the divine, and the special purveyors of the vital principles . . . and everywhere to be able to understand the language of birds was equivalent to being able to converse with the gods.[4]

If this is true it is not surprising that savages in various parts of the world trace their tribal origin to a supernatural bird of the same form and name as some familiar local species, which was inhabited by the soul of their heroic "first man." The Osage Indians of Kansas, for example, say that as far back as they can conceive of time their ancestors were alive, but had neither bodies nor souls. They existed beneath the lowest of the four "upper worlds," and at last migrated to the highest, where they obtained souls. Then followed travels in which they searched for some source whence they might get human bodies, and at last asked the question of a redbird sitting on her nest. She replied: "I can cause your children to have human bodies from my own." She explained that her wings would be their arms, her head their head, and so on through a long list of parts, external and internal, showing herself a good comparative anatomist. Finally she declared: "The speech (or breath) of children will I bestow on your children." [5]

Such is the story of how humanity reached the earth, according to one branch of the Osages: other gentes also believe themselves descended from birds that came down from an upper world. Dozens of similar cases might be quoted, of which I will select one because of its curious features. The Seri, an exclusive and backward tribe inhabiting the desert-like island Tiburon, in the Gulf of California, ascribe the creation of the world, and of themselves in particular, to the Ancient of Pelicans, a mythical fowl of supernal wisdom and melodious song— an unexpected poetic touch!—who first raised the earth above the primeval waters. This last point is in conformity with the general belief that a waste of waters preceded the appearance, by one or another miraculous means well within the redman's range of experience, of a bit of land; and it is to be observed that this original patch of earth, whether fixed or floating, was enlarged to habitable dimensions not by further miracles, nor by natural accretion, but, as a rule, by the labor and ingenuity of the "first men" themselves, usually aided by favorite animals. Thus the Seri Indians naturally held the pelican in especial regard, but that did not prevent their utilizing it to the utmost. Dr. W J McGee[6] found that one of their customs was to tie a broken-winged, living pelican to a stake near the seashore, and then appropriate the fishes brought to the captive by its free relatives.

In fewer cases we find that not only tribal but also individual origin is ascribed to a bird, the best illustration of which is the notion of the natives of Perak, in the Malay Peninsula, that a bird brings the soul to every person at birth. A woman who is about to become a mother selects as the place where her baby shall be born the foot of a certain tree—any one that appeals to her fancy—and this will be the "name-tree" of her child. The parents believe that a soul has been waiting for this child in the form of a bird that for some time before the birth frequents all the trees of the chosen kind in that vicinity, searching for the occasion when it may deliver its charge, intrusted to it by Kari, the tribal god. This bird must be killed and eaten by the expectant mother just before the actual birth or the baby will never come to life, or if it does will speedily die. A poetic feature in this tender explanation of the mystery of life among the jungle-dwellers is that the souls of first-born children are brought always by the newly hatched offspring of the bird that contained the soul of the mother of the child.[7]

Apart from this singular conception of the source of existence, the general theory of spirituality in birds is based, as heretofore intimated, on the almost universal belief that they are often the visible spirits of the dead. The Powhatans of Virginia, for example, held that the feathered race received the souls of their chiefs at death; and a California tribe asserted that the small birds whose hard luck it was to receive the souls of bad men were chased and destroyed by hawks, so that those of good Indians alone reached the happy hunting-grounds beyond the sky.

James G. Swan relates in his interesting old book about early days at Puget Sound, [10] that the Indians at Shoal-water Bay, Oregon, were much disturbed one morning because they had heard the whistling of a plover in the night. The white men there told them it was only a bird's crying, but they insisted the noise was that of spirits. Said they: "Birds don't talk in the night; they talk in the daytime." "But," asked Russell, "how can you tell that it is the *memelose tillicums,* or dead people? They can't talk." "No," replied the savage, "it is true they can't talk as we do, but they whistle through their teeth. You are a white man and do not understand what they say, but Indians know."

This bit of untainted savage philosophy recalls the queer British superstition of the Seven Whistlers. Wordsworth, who was a North-countryman, records of his ancient Dalesman—

> He the seven birds hath seen that never part,
> Seen the Seven Whistlers on their nightly rounds
> And counted them.

The idea that the wailing of invisible birds is a warning of danger direct from Providence prevails especially in the English colliery districts, where wildfowl, migrating at night and calling to one another as they go, supply exactly the right suggestion to the timid. Sailors fear them as "storm-bringers." Even more horrifying is the primitive Welsh conception (probably capable of a similar explanation) of the Three Birds of Rhiannon, wife of Pwyll, ruler of Hades, that could sing the dead to life and the living into the sleep of death. Luckily they were heard only at the death of great heroes in battle.

How easily such things may beguile the imagination is told in Thomas W. Higginson's book on army life in the black regiment of which he was the colonel during the Civil War. This sane and vigorous young officer writes of an incident on the South Carolina Coast: "I remember that, as I stood on deck in the still and misty evening, listening with strained senses for some sound of approach of an expected boat, I heard a low continuous noise from the distance, more mild and desolate than anything my memory can parallel. It came from within the vast circle of mist, and seemed like the cry of a myriad of lost souls upon the horizon's verge; it was Dante become audible: yet it was but the accumulated cries of innumerable seafowl at the entrance of the outer bay." [9]

But I have rambled away along an enticing by-path, as will frequently happen in the remainder of this book —to the reader's interest, I venture to believe.

Returning to the theme of a moment ago, I recall that the Rev. H. Friend [11] tells us that he has seen Buddhist priests in Canton "bless a small portion of their rice, and place it at the door of the refectory to be eaten by the birds which congregate there." These offerings are to the "house spirits," by which the Chinese mean the spirits of their ancestors, who are still kindly interested in the welfare of the family. This is real ancestor-worship expressed in birds; and Spence [12] records that "the shamans of certain tribes of Paraguay act as go-betweens between the members of their tribes and such birds as they imagine enshrine the souls of their departed relatives." The heathen Lombards ornamented their grave-posts with the effigy of a dove. This notion of birds as reincarnated human souls is not confined to untutored minds nor to an ancient period. Evidences of its hold on the human imagination may be found in Europe down to the present day, and it animates one of the most picturesque superstitions of pious followers of Mahomet, two forms of which have come to me. The first is given by Doughty,[13] the second by Keane,[14] both excellent authorities.

Doughty says: "It was an ancient opinion of the idolatrous Arabs that the departing spirit flitted from man's brainpan as a wandering fowl, complaining thenceforward in perpetual thirst her unavenged wrong; friends, therefore, to avenge the friend's soul-bird, poured upon the grave their pious libations of wine. The bird is called a 'green fowl.' "

Quoting Keane: "It is a superstition among the Mohammedans that the spirits of martyrs are lodged in the crops of green birds, and partake of the fruit and drink of the rivers of paradise; also that the souls of the good dwell in the form of white birds near the throne of God."

But the spirits represented in birds are not always ancestral or benevolent: they may be unpleasant, foreboding, demoniac. The Indians and negroes along the Amazons will not destroy goatsuckers. Why? Because they are receptacles for departed human souls who have come back to earth unable to rest because of crimes done in their former bodies, or to haunt cruel and hard-hearted masters. In Venezuela and Trinidad the groan-like cries of the nocturnal, cave-dwelling guacharos are thought to be the wailing of ghosts compelled to stay in their caverns in order to expiate their sins. Even now, the Turks maintain that the dusky shearwaters that daily travel in mysterious flocks up and down the Bosphorus are animated by condemned human souls.

By way of the ancestral traditions sketched above, arise those "sacred animals" constantly mentioned in accounts of ancient or backward peoples. Various birds were assigned to the deities and heroes of Egyptian and Pagan mythology—the eagle to Jove, goose and later the peacock to Juno, the little owl to Minerva, and so on; but to call these companions "sacred" is a bad use of the term, for there was little or nothing consecrate in these ascriptions, and if in any case worship was addressed to the deity, its animal companion was hardly included in the reverential thought of the celebrant.

It is conceivable that such ascriptions as these are the refined relics of earlier superstitions held by primitive folk everywhere in regard to such birds of their territory as appealed to their imaginations because of one or another notable trait. Ethnological and zoölogical books abound in instances, which it would be tedious to catalog, and several examples appear elsewhere in this book. A single, rather remarkable one, that of the South African ground-hornbill or bromvogel, will suffice to illustrate the point here. I choose, among several available, the account given by Layard,[15] one of the early naturalist-explorers in southern Africa:

The Fingoes seem to attach some superstitious veneration to the ground-hornbills and object to their being shot in the neighborhood of their dwellings, lest they should lose their

cattle by disease. . . . The Kaffirs have a superstition that if
one of these birds is killed it will rain for a long time. I am
told that in time of drought it is the custom to take one alive,
tie a stone to it, then throw it into a "vley"; after that a rain is
supposed to follow. They avoid using the water in which this
ceremony has been performed. . . . Only killed in time of
severe drought, when one is killed by order of the rain-doctor
and its body is thrown into a pool in a river. The idea is that
the bird has so offensive a smell that it will make the water
sick, and that the only way of getting rid of this is to wash it
away to the sea, which can only be done by a heavy rain.

The ground where they feed is considered good for cattle,
and in settling a new country spots frequented by these birds
are chosen by the wealthy people. Should the birds, however,
by some chance, fly over a cattle kraal, the kraal is moved to
some other place. . . . It is very weak on the wing, and when
required by the "doctor" the bird is caught by the men of a
number of kraals turning out at the same time, and a particular
bird is followed from one hill to another by those on the look-
out. After three or four flights it can be run down and caught
by a good runner. . . . The Ovampos [of Damara land] seem
to have a superstition [that the eggs cannot be procured because
so soft that] they would fall to pieces on the least handling.

It seems to me likely that the sense of service to men
in its constant killing of dreaded snakes—birds and serpents are linked together in all barbaric religious and
social myths—may be at the core of the veneration paid
the hornbill, as, apparently, it was in the case of the
Egyptian ibis. This wader was not only a foe to lizards
and small snakes, but, as it always appeared in the Nile
just as the river showed signs of beginning its periodic
overflow, a matter of anxious concern to the people, it
was regarded as a prescient and benevolent creature foretelling the longed-for rise of the water. At Hermopolis,
situated at the upper end of the great fertile plain of
the lower Nile, the ibis was incarnated as Thoth (identified by the Greeks with Hermes), one of the highest gods

of the ancient Egyptians. This ibis, and other incarnated animals, originally mere symbols of lofty ideas, came to be reverenced as real divinities in the places where their cult flourished (although they might enjoy no such distinction elsewhere), were given divine honors when they died, and were, in short, real gods to their devotees; that is to say, the sophisticated Egyptians of the later dynasties had elevated into the logical semblance of divinity this and that animal-fetish of their uncultured ancestors.

Another singular case of a bird rising to the eminence of tutelary deity is that of the ruddy sheldrake (*Casarca rutila*) or Brahminy duck in Thibet. From it is derived the title of the established church of the lamas (practically the government of that Buddhistic country); and their abbotts wear robes of the sheldrake colors. In Burmah the Brahminy duck is sacred to Buddhists as a symbol of devotion and fidelity, and it was figured on Asoka's pillars in this emblematic character. This sheldrake is usually found in pairs, and when one is shot the other will often hover near until it, too, falls a victim to its conjugal love.[16]

A stage in this process of deification is given by Tylor in describing the veneration of a certain bird in Polynesia, as a Tahitian priest explained it to Dr. Ellis, the celebrated missionary-student of the South Seas. The priest said that his god was not always in the idol representing it. "A god," he declared, "often came to and passed from an image in the body of a bird, and spiritual influence could be transmitted from an idol by imparting it by contact to certain valued kinds of feathers." This bit of doctrine helps us to understand what Colonel St. Johnston has to tell in his recent thoughtful book[48] on the ethnology of Polynesia, of the special use of the feathers (mainly red) of particular birds in the insignia of chiefs, and in religious ceremonials; and he comments as follows:

In the Samoa, Fiji, and Tonga groups the very special mats of the chiefs were edged with the much-prized red feathers usually obtained with great difficulty from Taverni Island. . . . In Tahiti the fan was associated with feathers in a peculiar idea of sacredness, and feathers given out by the priests at the temple at the time of the "Pa'e-atua" ceremony were taken home by the worshippers and tied on to special fans. These beautiful feathers of the Pacific were, of course, prized by an artistic people for their colors alone, but there seems to have been something more than that, something particularly connected with a divine royalty. In Hawaii the *kahili*, the sceptre of the king, was surmounted with special feathers. The royal cloaks (as in Peru) and the helmets had feathers thickly sewn on them; the *para-kura*, or sacred coronet of Tangier was made of red feathers; and the Pa'e-atua ceremony that I have just written of consisted of the unwrapping of the images of the gods, exposing them to the sun, oiling them, and then wrapping them once more in feathers—fresh feathers, brought by the worshippers, and given in exchange for the old ones, which were taken away as prized relics to be fastened to the sacred fans.

Can it be that the feathers represent divine birds, symbolic of the "Sky People"? We know that many birds were peculiarly sacred (the tropic bird of Fiji might be mentioned among others), and the messages of the gods were said to have been at first transmitted by the birds, until the priests were taught to do so in the squeaky voices—possibly imitative of bird-cries—they adopted.

Such deifications of birds took place elsewhere than in Fiji and Egypt. Charles de Kay has written a learned yet readable book [18] devoted to expounding the worship of birds in ancient Europe, and their gradual mergence into deities of human likeness. He calls attention to remains in early European lore indicating a very extensive connection of birds with gods, pointing to a worship of the bird itself as the living representative of a god, "or else to such a position of the bird toward a deity as to fairly permit the inference that at a period still more remote the bird itself was worshipped." The Polynesian practices detailed above certainly are of very ancient origin, probably coming to the islands with the earliest migrants from the East Indian mainlands; and the theology involved may be a lingering relic of the times and ideas described in De Kay's treatise.

To carry these matters further is not within my plan, for they would lead us into the mazes of comparative mythology, which it is my purpose to avoid as far as possible, restricting myself to history, sayings, and allusions that pertain to real, not imaginary, birds.*

The distinction I try to make between the mythical and the legendary or real, may be illustrated by the kingfisher—in this case, of course, the common species of southern Europe. Let us consider first the mythical side. Alcyone, daughter of Æolus, the wind-god, impelled by love for her husband Ceyx, whom she found dead on the shore after a shipwreck, threw herself into the sea. The gods, rewarding their conjugal love, changed the pair into kingfishers. What connection exists between this, which is simply a classic yarn, and the ancient theory of the nidification of this species, I do not know; but the story was—now we are talking of the real bird, which the Greeks and Latins saw daily—that the kingfisher hatched its eggs at the time of the winter solstice in a nest shaped like a hollow sponge, and thought to be

---

* Nevertheless, I have made one exception by devoting a chapter to "a fabulous flock" of wholly fictitious birds, namely, the phenix, rukh (roc), simurgh and their fellows—all hatched from the same solar nest—because they have become familiar to us, by name, at least, in literature, symbolism, and proverbial sayings.

solidly composed of fish-bones, which was set afloat, or
at any rate floated, on the surface of the Mediterranean.
The natural query how such a structure could survive the
shock of waves led to the theory that Father Æolus made
the winds "behave" during the brooding-time. As Pliny
explains: "For seven days before the winter solstice, and
for the same length of time after it, the sea becomes calm
in order that the kingfishers may rear their young."
Simonides, Plutarch, and many other classic authorities,
testify to the same tradition, which seems to have belonged particularly to the waters about Sicily. More
recent writers kept alive the tender conceit.

> Along the coast the mourning halcyon's heard
> Lamenting sore her spouse's fate,

are lines from Ariosto's verse almost duplicated by
Camoens; and Southey—

> The halcyons brood around the foamless isles,
> The treacherous ocean has forsworn its wiles.

while Dryden speaks of "halcyons brooding on a winter
sea," and Drayton makes use of the legend in five different poems. It is a fact that in the region of southern
Italy a period of calm weather ordinarily follows the
blustering gales of late autumn, which may have suggested this poetic explanation; but one student believes
that the story may have been developed from a far earlier
tradition. "The Rhibus of Aryan mythology, storm-
demons, slept for twelve nights [and days] about the
winter solstice . . . in the house of the sun-god Savitar."
Such is the history behind our proverbial expression
for tranquillity, and often it has been used very remotely

from its original sense, as when in *Henry VI* Shakespeare
makes La Pucelle exclaim: "Expect St. Martin's summer, halcyon days," St. Martin's summer being the
English name for that warm spell in November known to
us as Indian summer. All this is an extended example
of the kind of poetic myth which has been told of many
different birds, and which in this book is left to be sought
out in treatises on mythology.

In contrast with this sort of tale I find many non-
mythical notions, historical or existing, concerning the
actual kingfisher, which properly belong to my scheme.
One of the oldest is the custom formerly in vogue in
England, and more recently in France, of turning this
bird into a weathercock. The body of a mummified kingfisher with extended wings would be suspended by a
thread, nicely balanced, in order to show the direction
of the wind, as in that posture it would always turn its
beak, even when hung inside the house, toward the point
of the compass whence the breeze blew. Kent, in *King
Lear,* speaks of rogues who

> Turn their halcyon beaks
> With every gale and vary of their masters.

And after Shakespeare Marlowe, in his *Jew of Malta,*
says:

> But how stands the wind?
> Into what corner peers my halcyon's bill?

We are told that the fishermen of the British and French
coasts hang these kingfisher weathervanes in the rigging
of their boats; and it seems likely to me that it was among
sailors that the custom began.

Although Sir Thomas Browne [33] attributed "an occult and secret property" to this bird as an indicator of wind-drift, it does not otherwise appear that it had any magical reputation: yet the skin of a kingfisher was sure to be found among the stuffed crocodiles, grinning skulls and similar decorations of the consulting-room of a medieval "doctor," who himself rarely realized, perhaps, what a fakir he was. Moreover, we read "That its dried body kept in a house protected against lightning and kept moths out of garments."

On the American continent, probably the nearest approach to the "sacredness" discussed in a former paragraph, is the sincere veneration of their animal-gods, including a few birds, by the Zuñis and some other Village Indians of New Mexico and Arizona, which has been studied minutely by our ethnologists. Yet we read of many other sacred birds among the redmen. The red-headed woodpecker is regarded as the tutelary deity of the Omahas, and as the patron-saint of children, because, they say, its own family is kept in so safe a place. Pawnees have much the same sentiment toward the wren, which they call "laughing-bird" because it seems always happy. The crow was the sacred bird of the "ghost-dance"—a religious ceremony of high significance among the tribes of the Plains, as is explained in Chapter IX. The Navahos regard the mountain bluebird as sacred on account of its azure plumage, which (as something blue) is representative of the South; and it is deemed the herald of the rising sun, which is their supreme image of God. One of their old men told Stewart Culin that "two blue birds stand at the door of the house in which [certain] gods dwell."

In most cases among our Indians, as elsewhere, it is un-

lawful to kill or eat such a bird, which indicates a relation to totemism. Thus, as Powers [19] asserts, the Mono
Indians of the Sierra Nevada, never kill their sacred black
eagles, but pluck out the feathers of those that die and
wear them on their heads. "When they succeed in capturing a young one, after a fortnight the village makes a
great jubilation." Some Eskimos will not eat gulls'
eggs, which make men old and decrepit.

Whatever tradition or superstition or other motive
affected the choice of any bird as a tribal totem, or endowed it with "sacredness," practical considerations were
surely influential. It is noticeable that the venerated ibis
and hawk in Egypt were useful to the people as devourers
of vermin—young crocodiles, poisonous snakes, grain-
eating mice and so forth. Storks in Europe and India,
and the "unclean" birds of Palestine forbidden to the
Jews, were mostly carrion-eaters, and as such were de-
sirable street-cleaners in village and camp. A tradition
in the Ægean island Tenos is that Poseidon—a Greek St.
Patrick—sent storks to clear the island of snakes, which
originally were numerous there. Australian frontiers-
men preserve the big kingfisher, dubbed "laughing-jack-
ass," for the same good reason. The wiser men in early
communities appreciated this kind of service by birds,
and added a religious sanction to their admonition that
such servants of mankind should not be killed. It was the
primitive movement toward bird-protection, which, by
the way, was first applied in this country to the scaveng-
ing turkey-buzzards and carrion-crows of the Southern
States.

As for the smaller birds, where special regard was
paid them it was owing, apart from the natural humane
admiration and enjoyment of these pretty creatures, to

the mystery and fiction of their being animated by spirits. When they were black, like ravens and cormorants, or were cruel night-prowlers, such as owls, or uttered disconsolate cries, they were thought to be inhabited by dread, malignant, spirits "from night's Plutonian shore," as Poe expresses it, but when they had pretty plumage, pleasing ways and melodious voices, they were deemed the embodiment of beneficent and happy spirits—perhaps even those of departed relatives.

Hence we have the notion that some birds are lucky and others unlucky in their relation to us. Those that bring good luck are mainly those kinds that associate themselves with civilization, such as the various robins, wrens and storks, the doves and the swallows. Even so, however, time and place must be considered in every case, for the dearest of little birds when it pecks at a windowpane, or seems bent on entering a cottage door will arouse tremors of fear in a superstitious heart—much more so a bird that ordinarily keeps aloof from mankind. Frazer records, in his essay on Scapegoats, that if a wild bird flies into a rural Malay's house, it must be carefully caught and smeared with oil, and must then be released into the open air with a formula of words adjuring it to take away all ill-luck. In antiquity Greek women seem to have done the same with any swallow they found inside the house, a custom mentioned by both Pythagoras and Plato—the latter humorously proposing to dismiss poets from his ideal State in the same manner. Such doings remind one of the function of the scapegoat; and in fact, according to Frazer, the Hazuls, of the Carpathian Mountains, imagine they can transfer their freckles to the first swallow they see in the spring by uttering a certain command to the bird. Are these practices distorted reminiscences of the conjuring by the Hebrew shaman as described in the Old Testament?

This shall be the law of the leper in the day of his cleansing: He shall be brought into the priest. . . . Then shall the priest command to take for him that is to be cleaned two birds alive and clean, and cedar wood and scarlet and hyssop. And the priest shall command that one of the birds be killed in an earthen vessel over running water. As for the living bird, he shall take it and the cedar wood, and the scarlet, and the hyssop, and shall dip them and the living bird in the blood of the bird that was killed over the running water; and he shall sprinkle upon him that is to be cleansed from the leprosy seven times, and shall pronounce him clean, and shall let the living bird loose into the open field. (*Lev. xiv, 27.*)

The matter of "luck" in this hocus-pocus seems to lie in the chance as to which birds is chosen to be "scapegoat," and so is allowed to remain alive, cleaning its feathers as best it may. Evidently, the bird that wishes to do nothing to offend anyone must go warily. A cuckoo, for example, may spoil the day for an English milkmaid by incautiously sounding its call before her breakfast.

Such has been the mental attitude underlying the amazing ideas and practices that will be found described in succeeding chapters of this collection of traditional bird-lore, much of which is so juvenile and absurd. Until one reviews the groping steps by which mankind advanced with very uneven speed—a large body of it having yet hardly begun the progress, even among the "civilized" —from the crudest animism to a clearer and clearer comprehension of "natural law in the physical world," he cannot understand how men gave full credence to fictions that the most superficial examination, or the simplest reasoning, would show were false, and trembled before the most imaginary of alarms. Add to this childish credulity the teachings of religious and political leaders who had much to gain by conserving the ignorance and faith of their followers; add again the fruitful influence of story-tellers and poets who utilized ancient legends and beliefs for literary advantage, and you have the history and explanation of how so many primitive superstitions and errors have survived to our day.

CHAPTER II

BIRDS AS NATIONAL EMBLEMS

SEVERAL nations and empires of both ancient and modern times have adopted birds as emblems of their sovereignty, or at least have placed prominently on their coats of arms and great seals the figures of birds.

Among these the eagle—some species of the genus Aquila—takes precedence both in time and in importance. The most ancient recorded history of the human race is that engraved on the tablets and seals of chiefs who organized a civilization about the head of the Persian Gulf more than 4000 years before the beginning of the Christian era. These record by both text and pictures that the emblem of the Summerian city of Lagash, which ruled southern Mesopotamia long previous to its subjugation by Babylonia about 3000 B. C., was an eagle "displayed," that is, facing us with wings and legs spread and its head turned in profile. This figure was carried by the army of Lagash as a military standard; but a form of it with a lion's head was reserved as the special emblem of the Lagash gods, with which the royal house was identified—the king's standard.

After the conquest of Babylonia by Assyria this eagle of Lagash was taken over by the conquerors, and appears on an Assyrian seal of the king of Ur many centuries later. "From this eagle," says Ward,[23] "in its heraldic attitude necessitated by its attack on two animals [as

represented on many seals and decorations] was derived
the two-headed eagle, in the effort to complete the
bilateral symmetry. This double-headed eagle appears
in Hittite art, and is continued down through Turkish and
modern European symbolism."

Among the host of rock-carvings in the Eyuk section
of the mountains of Cappadocia (Pteria of the Greeks)
that are attributed to the Hittites, Perrot and Chipiez
found carvings of a double-headed eagle which they
illustrate;[112] and they speak of them as often occurring.
"Its position is always a conspicuous one—about a great
sanctuary, the principal doorway to a palace, a castle
wall, and so forth; rendering the suggestion that the
Pterians used the symbol as a coat of arms."

Dr. Ward thought the Assyrian two-headed figure of
their national bird resulted from an artistic effort at
symmetry, balancing the wings and feet outstretched on
each side, but I cannot help feeling that here among the
Hittites it had its origin in a deeper sentiment than that.
It seems to me that it was a way of expressing the dual
sex of their godhead, presupposed, in the crudeness of
primitive nature-worship, to account for the condition
of earthly things, male and female uniting for productiveness—the old story of sky and earth as co-generators of
all life. Many other symbols, particularly those of a
phallic character, were used in Asiatic religions to typify
the same idea; or perhaps the conception was of that
divine duality, in the sense of co-equal power of Good
and Evil, God and Satan, that later became so conspicuous
in the doctrine of the ancient Persians. Could it have
been a purified modification of this significance that made
the eagle during the Mosaic period—if Bayley [24] is right
—an emblem of the Holy Spirit? And Bayley adds

that "its portrayal with two heads is said to have re-corded the double portion of the spirit bestowed on Elisha."

Old Mohammedan traditions, according to Dalton, give the name "hamca" to a fabulous creature identical with the bicephalous eagle carved on Hittite rock-faces. Dalton [25] says also that coins with this emblem were struck and issued by Malek el Sala Mohammed, one of the Sassanids, in 1217; and that this figure was engraved in the 13th century by Turkoman princes on the walls of their castles, and embroidered on their battle-flags.

To the early Greeks the eagle was the messenger of Zeus. If, as asserted, it was the royal cognizance of the Etruscans, it came naturally to the Romans, by whom it was officially adopted for the Republic in 87 B. C., when a silver eagle, standing upright on a spear, its wings half raised, its head in profile to the left, and thunderbolts in its claws, was placed on the military standards borne at the head of all the legions in the army. This was in the second consulship of Caius Marius, who decreed certain other honors to be paid to the bird's image in the Curia.

One need not accuse the Romans of merely copying the ancient monarchies of the East. If they thought of any-thing beyond the majestic appearance of the noble bird, it was to remember its association with their great god Jupiter—the counterpart of Zeus. Nothing is plainer as to the origin of the ideas that later took shape in the divinities of celestial residence than that Jupiter was the personification of the heavens; and what is more natural than that the lightnings should be conceived of as his weapons? Once, early in his history, when Jupiter was equipping himself for a battle with the Titans, an eagle brought him his dart, since which time Jupiter's eagle has always been represented as holding thunderbolts in its talons. The bird thus became a symbol of supreme power, and a natural badge for soldiers. The emperors of imperial Rome retained it on their standards, Hadrian changing its metal from silver to gold; and "the eagles of Rome" came to be a common figure of speech to express her military prowess and imperial sway.

By such a history, partly mythical, and partly practical and glorious, this bird came to typify imperialism in general. A golden eagle mounted on a spear, was the royal standard of the elder Cyrus, as it had been of his ancestors.

When Napoleon I. dreamed of universal conquest he revived on the regimental banners of his troops the insignia of his Roman predecessors in banditry—in fact he was entitled to do so, for he had inherited them by right of conquest from both Italy and Austria, the residuary legatees of Rome. Discontinued in favor of their family bees by the Bourbons, during their brief reign after the fall of Bonaparte, the eagle was restored to France by a decree of Louis Napoleon in 1852. There is a legend that a tame eagle was let loose before him when he landed in France from England to become President of the first French Republic. Now it is the proper finial for flagstaffs all over the world except, curiously, in France itself, where a wreath of laurel legally surmounts the tricolor of the Republic, which has discarded all reminders of royalty. Thus the pride of conquerors has dropped to the commonplace of fashion—

> Imperial Caesar, dead and turned to clay,
> Might stop a hole to keep the wind away.

The destruction of the Italian and western half of the old Roman empire was by the hands of northern barbarians who at first were mere conquerors and despoilers, but finally, affected by their contact with civilization and law, became residents in and rulers of Italy, and were proud to assume the titles and what they could of the dignity of Roman emperors. In the eighth century Charlemagne became substantially master of the western world, at least, and assumed the legionary eagle as he did the purple robes of an Augustus; and his successors held both with varying success until the tenth century, when German kings became supreme and in 962 founded that very unholy combination styled the Holy Roman Empire. For hundreds of years this fiction was maintained. At times its eagle indicated a real lordship over all Europe; between times the states broke apart, and, as each kept the royal standard, separate eagles contended for mastery. Thus Prussia and other German kingdoms retained on their shields the semblance of a "Roman" eagle; and the Teutonic Knights carried it on their savage expeditions of "evangelization" to the eastern Baltic lands.

All these were more or less conventional figures of the Bird of Jove in its natural form, but a heraldic figure with two heads turned, Janus like, in opposite directions, was soon to be revived in the region where, as we have seen, it had been familiar 2000 years before as the national emblem of the Eastern, or Byzantine, Empire, which for hundreds of years contested with Rome, both the political and the ecclesiastical hegemony of the world. Just when this symbol came into favor at Constantinople is unknown, but one authority says it did not appear before the tenth century. At that time the Eastern emperors were recovering lost provinces and extending their

rule until it included all the civilized part of western Asia,
Greece, Bulgaria, southern Italy, and much of the islands
and shores of the Mediterranean; and they asserted religious supremacy, at least, over the rival European empire erected on Charlemagne's foundation. It would
seem natural that at this prosperous period, when
Byzantium proudly claimed, if she did not really possess
all "the glory that was Greece and the grandeur that
was Rome," such a double-headed device might be
adopted, signifying that she had united the western power
with her own. The evidence of this motive is doubtful,
however, for it is not until a much later date that the
figure begins to be seen on coins and textiles, first at
Trebizond, particularly in connection with the emperor
Theodore Lascaris, who reigned at the beginning of the
13th century. Dalton [25] suggests plausibly that this
symbol may have become Byzantine through the circumstance that this Lascaris had previously been despot of
Nicomedia, in which province Bogaz-Keui and other
Hittite remains were situated, and where the bicephalous
carvings heretofore alluded to are still to be seen on rock-
faces and ruins, always in association with royalty.

It is very attractive to think that this form of eagle
was chosen, as has been suggested, to express the fact
that Constantinople was now lord over both halves, East
and West, into which Diocletian had divided the original
empire of Rome. Whether this idea was behind the
choice I do not know, but at any rate the two-faced
eagle became latterly the acknowledged ensign of imperial
Byzantium, and as such was introduced into European
royal heraldry, whether or not by means of the returning
Crusaders, as commonly stated, remains obscure.

In the 15th century what was left of the Holy Roman

Empire became the heritage of the Austrian house of Hapsburg which had succeeded the German Hohenstauffens; and to Sigismund, head of the house in that century, is ascribed the design in the Austrian arms of the two-headed eagle, looking right and left, as if to signify boastfully that he ruled both East and West. These were relative and indefinite domains, but as he had, by his crowning at Rome, received at least nominal sovereignty over the fragmentary remains in Greece of the ancient Eastern Empire, he was perhaps justified in adopting the Byzantine ensign as "captured colors"; but a rival was soon to present a stronger claim to these fragments and their badge.

In this same period, that is in the middle of the 15th century, Ivan the Great of Russia was striving with high purpose and despotic strength to bring back under one sway the divided house of Muscovy, together with whatever else he could obtain. To further this purpose he married, in 1472, Sophia Paleologos, niece of the last Byzantine emperor, getting with her Greece and hence a barren title to the throne of the Eastern empire—a barren title because its former domain was now over-run by the Turks, but very important in the fact that it included the headship of the Greek, or Orthodox, Church. From this time Russia as well as Austria has borne a two-faced eagle on its escutcheon; and, although both birds are from the same political nest, the feeling between them has been far from brotherly.

It may be remarked here, parenthetically, that in Egypt the cult of the kingly eagle never flourished, for the griffon vulture, "far-sighted, ubiquitous, importunate," became the grim emblem of royal power; and a smaller vulture (*Neophron percnopterus*) is called Pharaoh's chicken to this day by the fellaheen. By "eagle" in Semitic (Biblical) legends is usually meant the lammergeier.

Prussia had kept a single-headed eagle as her cognizance in remembrance of her previous "Roman" greatness; and it was retained by the German Empire when that was created by Bismarck half a century and more ago. From it the Kaiser designated the two German military orders—the Black Eagle and the superior Red Eagle; and Russia and Serbia have each instituted an order called White Eagle. The traditional eagle of Poland is represented as white on a black ground. It was displayed during the period of subjection following the partition of the country in 1795, with closed wings, but now, since 1919, it spreads its pinions wide in the pride of freedom.

In the years between 1914 and 1919 an allied party of hunters, enraged by their depredations, went gunning for these birds of prey, killed most of them and sorely wounded the rest!

Although several species of real eagles inhabit the Mediterranean region and those parts of Europe and Asia where these nations lived, and warred, and passed away, and are somewhat confused in the mass of myth and tradition relating to them, the one chosen by Rome was the golden eagle, so called because of the golden gloss that suffuses the feathers of the neck in mature birds. Now we have this species of sea-eagle in the United States, and it has been from time immemorial the honored War-eagle of the native redmen. If it was needful at our political birth to put any sort of animal on our seal, and the choice was narrowed down to an eagle, it would have been far more appropriate to have chosen the golden rather than the white-headed or "bald" species—first be-

cause the golden is in habits and appearance far the nobler
of the two, and, second, because of the supreme regard
in which it was held by all the North American aborigines, who paid no respect whatever to the bald eagle. On
the other hand, the white head and neck of our accepted
species gives a distinctive mark to our coat of arms.
The history of the adoption of this symbol of the United
States of America is worth a paragraph.

On July 4, 1776, on the afternoon following the morning hours in which the Congress in Philadelphia had
performed the momentous duty of proclaiming the independence of the United States, it dropped down to the
consideration of its cockade, and appointed a committee
to prepare a device for a Great Seal and coat-of-arms
for the new republic.[26] Desiring to avoid European
models, yet clinging to the traditions of art in these
matters, the committee devised and offered in succession
several complicated allegorical designs that were promptly
and wisely rejected by the Congress. Finally, in 1782, the
matter was left in the hands of Charles Thomson, Secretary of the Congress, and he at once consulted with
William Barton of Philadelphia. They abandoned
allegory and designed an eagle "displayed proper," that
is, with a shield on its breast. Mr. Barton, who was
learned in heraldry, explained that "the escutcheon being
placed on the breast of the eagle *displayed* is a very
ancient mode of bearing, and is truly imperial." To
avoid an "imperial" effect, however, a concession was
made to local prejudice by indicating plainly that the bird
itself was the American bald eagle—unless, indeed, that
happened to be the only one Barton knew!

This design was finally adopted in 1782. Since then
the Great Seal has been re-cut several times, so that the

bird in its imprint is now a far more reputable fowl than
at first—looks less as if it were nailed on a barn-door
pour encourager les autres. In its right claw it holds a
spray of ripe olives as an emblem of a peaceful disposition, and in its left an indication of resolution to en-
force peace, in the form of American thunderbolts—
the redman's arrows.

There were men in the Congress in 1782, as well as
out of it, who disliked using any eagle whatever as a
feature of the arms of the Republic, feeling that it
savored of the very spirit and customs against which the
formation of this commonwealth was a protest. Among
them stood that clear-headed master of common sense,
Benjamin Franklin, who thought a thoroughly native and
useful fowl, like the wild turkey, would make a far truer
emblem for the new and busy nation. He added to the
turkey's other good qualities that it was a bird of courage,
remarking, with his own delightful humor, that it would
not hesitate to attack any *Red*coat that entered its barnyard!

Franklin was right when he argued against the choice
of the bald eagle, at any rate, as our national emblem.
"He is," he said truly, "a bird of bad moral character;
he does not get his living honestly; you may have seen
him perched on some dead tree, where, too lazy to fish for
himself, he watches the labor of the fishing-hawk, and
when that diligent bird has at length taken a fish and is
bearing it to its nest the bald eagle pursues him and takes
it from him. Besides, he is a rank coward; the little
kingbird attacks him boldly. He is therefore by no means
a proper emblem."

None of these depreciatory things could Franklin have
truly said of the skilful, self-supporting, and handsome

golden eagle—a Bird of Freedom indeed. (Audubon named a western variety of it after General Washington.) This species was regarded with extreme veneration by the native redmen of this country. "Its feathers," says Dr. Brinton, the ethnologist, "composed the war-flag of the Creeks, and its image, carved in wood, or its stuffed skin, surmounted their council-lodges. None but an approved warrior dare wear it among the Cherokees, and the Dakotas allowed such an honor only to him who first touched the corpse of the common foe. The Natchez and other tribes regarded it almost as a deity. The Zuñi of New Mexico employed four of its feathers to represent the four winds when invoking the raingod."

Hence a war-song of the Ojibways reported by Schoolcraft:

> Hear my voice ye warlike birds!
> I prepare a feast for you to batten on;
> I see you cross the enemy's lines;
> Like you I shall go.
> I wish the swiftness of your wings;
> I wish the vengeance of your claws;
> I muster my friends;
> I follow your flight.

Doesn't this sound like a bit from the *Saga* of Harold Hadrada?

Mexico did better in choosing her crested eagle, the harpy (*Thrasaëtus harpia*), a magnificent representative of its race, renowned from Paraguay to Mexico for its handsome black-and-white plumage adorned with a warrior's crest, and for its grand flight, dauntless courage and amazing endurance. Quesada tells us that the Aztecs called it the winged wolf. The princes of Tlascala wore its image on their breasts and on their shield as a symbol of royalty; and in both Mexico and Peru, where it was trained for sport in falconry, it was preferred to the puma, which also was taught to capture deer and young peccaries for its master, as is the cheeta in India. Captive harpies are still set to fight dogs and wildcats in village arenas, and rarely are vanquished.

The tradition is that the Aztecs, a northern Nahuatl tribe, escaping from the tyranny of the dominant Chichemecas, moved about A. D. 1325 into the valley of Mexico (Tenochtitlan), and settled upon certain islets in a marshy lake—the site of the subsequent City of Mexico; and this safe site is said to have been pointed out to them by a sign from their gods—an eagle perched upon a prickly-pear cactus, the nopal, in the act of strangling a serpent. This is the picture Cortez engraved on his Great Seal, and Mexico has kept it to this day.

Guatemala was a part of ancient Mexico; and perched on the shield in Guatemala's coat-of-arms is the green or resplendent trogon (*Pharomacrus mocinno*), the native and antique name of which is quetzal. This is one of the most magnificent of birds, for its crested head and body (somewhat larger than a sparrow's) are iridescent green, the breast and under parts crimson, and the wings black overhung by long, plumy coverts. The quetzal's special ornament, however, is its bluish-green tail, eight or ten inches long, whose gleaming feathers curve down in the graceful sweep of a sabre. It has been called the most beautiful of American birds, and it is peculiar to Central America.

How this trogon came to be Guatemala's national symbol, made familiar by all its older postage-stamps, is a matter of religious history. One of the gods in the ancient Aztec pantheon was Quetzalcoatl, of whom it was said in their legends "that he was of majestic presence, chaste in life, averse to war, wise and generous in action, and delighting in the cultivation of the arts of peace." He was the ruler of the realm far below the surface of the earth, where the sun shines at night, the abode of abundance where dwell happy souls; and there Quetzal-coatl abides until the time fixed for his return to men. The first part of the name of this beneficent god, associated with sunshine and green, growing things, meant in the Nahuatl language a large, handsome, green feather, such as were highly prized by the Aztecs and reserved for the decoration of their chiefs; and one tradition of the god's origin and equipment relates that he was furnished with a beard made of these plumes. These royal and venerated feathers were obtained from the trogon, which his worshippers called *Quetzal-totl*. The emerald-hued hummingbirds of the tropics also belonged to him.

Although Mexico and Central America were "converted" to Christianity by a gospel of war and slavery, the ancient faith lived on in many simple hearts, especially in the remoter districts of the South, and nowhere more persistently than among the Mayas of Guatemala and Yucatan, whose pyramidal temples are moldering in their uncut forests. When, in 1825, Guatemala declared its independence and set up a local government, what more natural than that it should take as a national symbol the glorious bird that represented to its people the best influence in their ancient history and the most hopeful suggestion for the future.

In the religion of the Mayas of Yucatan the great god of light was Itsamna, one of whose titles was The Lord, the Eye of the Day—a truly picturesque description of the sun. A temple at Itzmal was consecrated to him

under the double name Eye of Day-Bird of Fire. "In
time of pestilence," as Dr. Brinton informs us,[27] "the
people resorted to this temple, and at high noon a sacrifice
was spread upon the altar. The moment the sun reached
the zenith a bird of brilliant plumage, but which in fact
was nothing else than a fiery flame shot from the sun, descended and consumed the offering in the sight of all."
Another authority says that Midsummerday was celebrated by similar rites. Hence was held sacred the flame-
hued ara, or guacamaya, the red macaw.

The Musicas, natives of the Colombian plateau where
Bogotá now stands, had a similar half-superstitious regard for this big red macaw, which they called "fire-bird."
The general veneration for redness, prevalent throughout
western tropical America, and in Polynesia, is doubtless
a reflection of sun-worship.

Let us turn to a lighter aspect of our theme.

France rejoices, humorously, yet sincerely, in the cock
as her emblem—the strutting, crowing, combative chanticleer that arouses respect while it tickles the French
sense of fun. When curiosity led me to inquire how this
odd representative for a glorious nation came into existence, I was met by a complete lack of readily accessible
information. The generally accepted theory seemed to
be that it was to be explained by the likeness of sound between the Latin word *gallus,* a dunghill cock, and *Gallus,*
a Gaul—the general appellative by which the Romans
of mid-Republic days designated the non-Italian, Keltic-
speaking inhabitants of the country south and west of
the Swiss Alps. But whence came the name "gaul"? and
why was a pun on it so apt that it has survived through long
centuries? I knew, of course, of the yarn that Diodorus
Siculus repeats: that in Keltica once ruled a famous man

who had a daughter "tall and majestic" but unsatisfactory
because she refused all the suitors who presented themselves. Then Hercules came along, and the haughty
maiden surrendered at Arras. The result was a son
named Galetes—a lad of extraordinary virtues who became king and extended his grandfather's dominions.
He called his subjects after his own name Galatians and
his country Galatia. This is nonsense. Moreover
"Galatia" is Greek, and was applied by the Greeks, long
before the day of Diodorus, to the lands of a colony of
Keltic-speaking migrants who had settled on the coast
of Asia Minor, and became the Galatians to whom Paul
wrote one of his *Epistles*. The Greek word *Galatai* was,
however, a form of the earlier *Keltai*.

As has been said, what we call Savoy and France
were known to the Romans as *Gallia,* Gaul; but this term
had been familiar in Italy long before Caesar had established Roman power over the great region between the
German forests and the sea that he tersely described as
Omnia Gallia; and it seems to have originated in the following way:

About 1100 B. C. two wild tribes, the Umbrians and
the Oscans, swept over the mountains from the northeast,
and took possession of northern Italy. These invaders
were Nordics, and used an antique form of Teutonic
speech. They were resisted, attacked, and finally over-
whelmed by the Etruscans, who about 800 B. C., when
Etruria was at the height of its power, extended their
rule to the Alps and the Umbrian State disappeared. In
the sixth century new hordes, calling themselves Kymri,
coming from the west, and speaking Keltic dialects,
swarmed into northern Italy from the present France.

The harried people north of the Po, themselves mostly descendants of the earlier invasion, spoke of these raiders by an old Teutonic epithet which the Romans heard and wrote as *Gallus,* the meaning of which was "stranger"—in this case "the enemy."

The word *Gallus,* Gaul or a Gaul, then, was an ancient Teutonic epithet inherited by the Romans from the Etruscans, and had in its origin no relation to *gallus,* the lord of the poultry-yard. It is most likely, indeed, that the term was given in contempt, as the Greeks called foreigners "barbarians" because they spoke some language which the Greeks did not understand; for the occupants of the valley of the Po at that time were of truly Germanic descent, and did not regard the round-headed, Alpine "Kelts" as kin in any sense, but rather as ancient foes. What the word on their lips actually was no one knows; but it seems to have had a root *gal* or *val,* interchangeable in the sound (to non-native ears) of its initial letter, whence it appears that Galatai, Gael, Valais, Walloon, and similar names connected with Keltic history are allied in root-derivation. Wales, for example, to the early Teutonic immigrants into Britain was the country of the *Wealas, i.e.,* the "foreigners" (who were Gaulish, Keltic-speaking Kymri); and the English are not yet quite free from that view of the Welsh.

The opportunity to pun with *gallus,* a cock, is evident, just as was a bitter pun current in Martial's time between *Gallia,* a female Gaul and *gallia,* a gall-nut; but in all this there is nothing to answer the question why the pun of which we are in search—if there was such a pun—has endured so long. I think the answer lies in certain appearances and customs of the Keltic warriors.

Plutarch, in his biography of Caius Marius, describes the Kymri fought by Marius, years before Caesar's campaigns, as wearing helmets surmounted by animal effigies of various kinds, and many tall feathers. Diodorus says the Gauls had red hair, and made it redder by dyeing it with lime. This fierce and flowing red head-dress must have appeared much like a cock's comb, to which the vainglorious strutting of the barbarians added a most realistic touch in the eyes of the disciplined legion-aries. Later, the Roman authorities in Gaul minted a coin or coins bearing a curious representation of a Gaulish helmet bearing a cock on its crest, illustrations of which are printed by G. R. Rothery in his *A B C of Heraldry*. Rothery also states that the bird appears on Gallo-Roman sculptures. Another writer asserts that Julius Caesar records that those Gauls that he encountered fought under a cock-standard, which he regarded as associated with a religious cult, but I have been unable to verify this interesting reference. Caesar does mention in his *Commentaries* that the Gauls were fierce fighters, and that one of their methods in personal combat was skilful kick-ing, like a game-cock's use of its spurs—a trick still em-ployed by French rowdies, and known as *la savate*. In the Romance speech of the south of France chanticleer is still *gall*.

The question arises here in the mind of the naturalist: If the aboriginal Gauls really bore a "cock" on their banners and wore its feathers in their helmets (as the Alpine regiments in Italy now wear chanticleer's tail-plumes), what bird was it? They did not then possess the Oriental domestic fowls to which the name properly belongs, and had nothing among their wild birds re-sembling it except grouse. One of these wild grouse is

the great black capercaille, a bold, handsome bird of
the mountain forests, noted for its habit in spring of
mounting a prominent tree and issuing a loud challenge to
all rivals; and one of its gaudy feathers is still the favorite ornament for his hat of the Tyrolean mountaineer.
By the way, the *cockade,* that figured so extensively as
a badge in the period of the French Revolution was so
called because of its resemblance to a cock's comb.

Now comes a break of several centuries in the record,
illuminated by only a brief note in La Rousse's *Encyclo-
pédie,* that in 1214, after the Dauphin du Viennois had
distinguished himself in combat with the English, an
order of knights was formed styled L'Ordre du Coq; and
that a white cock became an emblem of the dauphins of
the Viennois line.

The cock did not appear as a blazon when, after the
Crusades, national coats-of-arms were being devised;
nevertheless the *le coq de France* was not forgotten, for
it was engraved on a medal struck to celebrate the birth
of Louis XIII (1601). Then came the Revolution, when
the old régime was overthrown; and in 1792 the First
Republic put the cock on its escutcheon and on its flag
in place of the lilies of the fallen dynasty. When this
uprising of the people had been suppressed, and Napoleon
I had mounted the throne, in 1804, he substituted for it
the Roman eagle, which he had inherited from his conquests in Italy and Austria, and which was appropriate
to his ambitious designs for world domination. This remained until Napoleon went to Elba, and then Louis
XVIII brought back for a short time the Bourbon lilies;
yet medals and cartoons of the early Napoleonic era
depict the Gallic cock chasing a runaway lion of Castile
or a fleeing Austrian eagle, showing plainly what was

the accepted symbol of French power in the eyes of the common folks of France. One medal bore the motto *Je veille pour le nation.*

Napoleon soon returned from Elba only to be extinguished at Waterloo, after which, during the régime of Louis Philippe, the figure of the Gallic cock was again mounted on the top of the regimental flagstaffs in place of the gilded eagle; an illustration of this finial is given in *Armories et Drapeaux Français.* Louis Philippe could do this legitimately, according to Rothery and others, because this bird was the crest of his family—the Bourbons—in their early history in the south of France. The Gallic cock continued to perch on the banner-poles until the foundation of the second Empire under Louis Napoleon in 1852. Since then the "tricolor," originating in 1789 as the flag of the National Guard, and dispensing with all devices, has waved over France. Officially bold chanticleer was thus dethroned; but in the late World War, as in all previous periods of public excitement, the ancient image of French nationality has been revived, as the illustrated periodicals and books of the time show; and, much as they revere the tricolor, the soldiers still feel that it is *le coq Gaulois* that in 1918 again struck down the black eagles of their ancient foes.

Juvenal's sixth *Satire,* in which he castigates the Roman women of his day for their sins and follies, contains a line, thrown in as a mere side-remark—

> Rara avis in terris, negroque similima cygno—

which has become the most memorable line in the whole homily. It has been variously translated, most literally, perhaps, by Madan: "A rare bird in the earth, and very like a black swan." The comparison was meant to indicate something improbable to the point of absurdity; and in that sense has *rara avis* been used ever since.

For more than fifteen hundred years Juvenal's expression for extreme rarity held good; but on January 6, 1697, the Dutch navigator Willem de Vlaming, visiting the southwestern coast of Australia, sent two boats ashore to explore the present harbor of Perth. "There their crews first saw two and then more black swans, of which they caught four, taking two of them alive to Batavia; and Valentyne, who several years later recounted this voyage, gives in his work a plate representing the ship, boats and birds at the mouth of what is now known from this circumstance as Swan River, the most important stream of the thriving colony now State of Western Australia, which has adopted this very bird as its armorial symbol."

Another Australian bird, that, like the black swan, has obtained a picturesque immortality in a coat-of-arms; and on postage stamps, is the beautiful lyre-bird, first discovered in New South Wales in 1789, and now a feature in the armorial bearings of that State in the Australian Commonwealth. New Zealand's stamps show the apteryx (kiwi) and emeu.

One might extend this chapter by remarking on various birds popularly identified with certain countries, as the ibis with Egypt, the nightingale with England and Persia, the condor with Peru, the red grouse with Scotland, the ptarmigan with Newfoundland, and so on. Then might be given a list of birds whose feathers belonged exclusively to chieftanship, and so had a sort of tribal significance. Thus in Hawaii a honeysucker, the mamo, furnished for the adornment of chiefs alone the rich

yellow feathers of which "royal" cloaks were made; the
Inca "emperors" of Peru, before the Spanish conquest, reserved to themselves the rose-tinted plumage of an
Andean water-bird; an African chief affected the long
tail-plumes of the widowbird—and so forth.

Only one of these locally revered birds entices me to
linger a moment—the nightingale, beloved of English
poets, whose oriental equivalent is the Persian bulbul.
The mingled tragedies of the nightingale and the swallow
form the theme of one of the most famous as well as
sentimental legends of Greek mythology. These myths,
strangely confused by different narrators, have been un-
ravelled by the scholarly skill of Miss Margaret Verrall
in her *Mythology of Ancient Athens;*[108] and her analysis
throws light on the way the Greek imagination, from prehistoric bards down to the vase-decorators of the classic
era, and to the dramatists Sophocles, Æschylus, and
Aristophanes, dealt with birds—a very curious study.
Miss Verrall reminds us that a word is necessary as to
the names of the Attic tale. "We are accustomed, bur-
dened as we are with Ovidian association, to think of
Philomela as the nightingale. Such was not the version
of Apollodorus, nor, so far as I know, of any earlier
Greek writer. According to Apollodorus, Procne became
the nightingale ('αηδών) and Philomela the swallow (χελιδών)
It was Philomela who had her tongue cut out, a tale that
would never have been told of the nightingale, but which
fitted well with the short restless chirp of the swallow.
To speak a barbarian tongue was 'to mutter like a
swallow.' "

But there has arisen in Persia a literature of the nightingale, or "bulbul," springing from a pathetic legend—
if it is not simply poetic fancy—that as the bird pours
forth its song "in a continuous strain of melody" it is

pressing its breast against a rose-thorn to ease its heart's pain. Giles Fletcher, who had been attached to one of Queen Elizabeth's missions to Russia, and perhaps in that way picked up the suggestion, used it in one of his love-poems in a stanza that is a very queer mixture of two distinct fancies and a wrong sex, for the thrush that sings is not the one that has any occasion to weep about virginity:

> So Philomel, perched on an aspen sprig,
> Weeps all the night her lost virginity,
> And sings her sad tale to the merry twig,
> That dances at such joyful mystery.
> Ne ever lets sweet rest invade her eye,
> But leaning on a thorn her dainty chest
> For fear soft sleep should steal into her breast
> Expresses in her song grief not to be expressed.

The poetic vision over which Hafiz and others have sighed and sung in the fragrant gardens of Shiraz seems to owe nothing to the Greek tale, and to them the plaintive note in the bird's melody is not an expression of bitter woe, but only bespeaks regret whenever a rose is plucked. They will tell you tearfully that the bulbul will hover about a rosebush in spring, till, overpowered by the sweetness of its blossoms, the distracted bird falls senseless to the ground. The rose is supposed to burst into flower at the opening song of its winged lover. You may place a handful of fragrant herbs and flowers before the nightingale, say the Persian poets, yet he wishes not in his constant and faithful heart for more than the sweet breath of his beloved rose—

> Though rich the spot
> With every flower the earth has got,
> What is it to the nightingale
> If there his darling rose is not.

But romantic stories of the association of the queen of flowers with the prince of birds are many, and the reader may easily find more of them. In a legend told by the Persian poet Attarall the birds once appeared before King Solomon and complained that they could not sleep because of the nightly wailings of the bulbul, who excused himself on the plea that his love for the rose was the cause of irrepressible grief. This is the tradition to which Byron alludes in *The Giaour:*

> The rose o'er crag or vale,
> Sultana of the nightingale,
>   The maid for whom his melody,
>   His thousand songs, are heard on high,
> Blooms blushing to her lover's tale—
> His queen, the garden queen, the rose,
> Unbent by winds, unchilled by snows.

CHAPTER III

AN ORNITHOLOGICAL COMEDY OF ERRORS

AMONG the many proverbial expressions relating to birds, none, perhaps, is more often on the tongue than that which implies that the ostrich has the habit of sticking its head in the sand and regarding itself as thus made invisible. The oldest written authority known to me for this notion is the *Historical Library* of Diodorus Siculus. Describing Arabia and its products Diodorus writes:

> It produces likewise Beasts of a double nature and mixt Shape; amongst whom are those that are called *Struthocameli,* who have the Shape both of a Camel and an Ostrich . . . so that this creature seems both terrestrial and volatile, a Land-Beast and a Bird: But being not able to fly by reason of the Bulk of her body, she runs upon the Ground as Swift as if she flew in the air; and when she is pursued by Horsemen with her Feet she hurls the Stones that are under her, and many times kills the Pursuers with the Blows and Strokes they receive. When she is near being taken, she thrusts her Head under a Shrub or some such like Cover; not (as some suppose) through Folly or Blockishness, as if she would not see or be seen by them, but because her head is the tenderest Part of her Body.[109]

It would appear from this that Diodorus was anticipating me by quoting an ancient legend only to show how erroneous it was; but the notion has survived his explanation, and supplies a figure of speech most useful to polemic editors and orators, nor does anyone seem to care whether or not it expresses a truth. The only founda tion I can find or imagine for the origin of this so persistent and popular error in ornithology is that when the bird is brooding or resting it usually stretches its head and neck along the ground, and is likely to keep this prostrate position in cautious stillness as long as it thinks it has not been observed by whatever it fears. The futile trick of hiding its head alone has been attributed to various other birds equally innocent.

Ostriches in ancient times roamed the deserts of the East from the Atlas to the Indus, and they came to hold a very sinister position in the estimation of the early inhabitants of Mesopotamia, as we learn from the seals and tablets of Babylonia. There the eagle had become the type of the principle of Good in the universe, as is elsewhere described; and a composite monster, to which the general term "dragon" is applied, represented the principle of Evil. The earliest rude conception of this monster gave it a beast's body (sometimes a crocodile's but usually a lion's), always with a bird's wings, tail, etc. "From conceiving of the dragon as a monster having a bird's head as well as wings and tail, and feathers over the body, the transition," as Dr. Ward [23] remarks, "was not difficult to regard it entirely as a bird. But for this the favorite form was that of an ostrich . . . the largest bird known, a mysterious inhabitant of the deserts, swift to escape and dangerous to attack. No other bird was so aptly the emblem of power for mischief. . . . Accordingly, in the period of about the eighth to the seventh centuries, B. C., the contest of Marduk, representing Good in the form of a human hero or sometimes as an eagle, with an ostrich, or often a pair of them, representing the evil demon Tiamat, was a favorite subject

with Babylonian artists in the valleys of the Tigris and
Euphrates."

In view of their inheritance of these ideas it is no
wonder that Oriental writers far more recent told strange
tales about this bird, especially as to its domestic habits,
as is reflected in the book of Job, where a versified rendering of one passage (xxxix, 15, 16) runs thus:

> Gavest thou the goodly wings unto the peacocks?
> Or wings and feathers unto the ostrich?
> Which leaveth her eggs in the earth,
> And warmeth them in the dust,
> And forgetteth that the foot may crush them,
> Or that the wild beast may break them?
> She is hardened against her young ones
> As though they were not hers:
> Because God hath deprived her of wisdom,
> Neither hath he imparted to her understanding.

This was more elegant than exact, for ostriches are exceedingly watchful and patient parents, as they have need
to be, considering the perilous exposure of their nests on
the ground, and the great number of enemies to which
both eggs and young are exposed in the wilderness.
Major S. Hamilton,[110] than whom there is no better authority, testifies to this. "The hen-bird," he says, "sits
on the eggs by day and the cock relieves her at night,
so that the eggs are never left unguarded during incuba-
tion." The chicks are able to take care of themselves
after a day or two, and there is no more foundation in
fact for the Biblical charge of cruelty than for that other
Oriental fable that this bird hatches its eggs not by brooding but by the rays of warmth and light from her eyes.
"Both birds are employed," the fable reads, "for if the
gaze is suspended for only one moment the eggs are

addled, whereupon these bad ones are at once broken."
It is to this fiction that Southey refers in *Thalaba, the
Destroyer:*

> With such a look as fables say
> The mother ostrich fixes on her eggs,
> Till that intense affection
> Kindle its light of life.

Hence, as Burnaby tells us, ostrich eggs were hung in
some Mohammedan mosques as a reminder that "God
will break evil-doers as the ostrich her worthless eggs."
Professor E. A. Grosvenor notes in his elaborate volumes
on Constantinople, that in the turbeh of Eyouk, the
holiest building and shrine in the Ottoman world, are
suspended "olive lamps and ostrich eggs, the latter significant of patience and faith." Their meanings or at
any rate the interpretations vary locally, but the shells
themselves are favorite mosque ornaments all over Islam,
and an extensive trans-Saharan caravan-trade in them
still exists. Ostrich eggs as well as feathers were imported into ancient Egypt and Phœnicia from the Land
of Punt (Somaliland) and their shells have been recovered from early tombs, or sometimes clay models of
them, as at Hu, where Petrie found an example decorated
with an imitation of the network of cords by which it
could be carried about, just as is done to this day by the
Central-African negroes, who utilize these shells as water-
bottles, and carry a bundle of them in a netting bag.
Other examples were painted; and Wilkinson surmises
that these were suspended in the temples of the ancient
Egyptians as they now are in those of the Copts. The
Punic tombs about Carthage, and those of Mycenae, in
Greece, have yielded painted shells of these eggs; and

five were exhumed from an Etruscan tomb, ornamented with bands of fantastic figures of animals either engraved or painted on the shell, the incised lines filled with gold; what purpose they served, or whether any religious significance was attached to them, is not known. Eggs are still to be found in many Spanish churches hanging near the Altar: they are usually goose-eggs, but may be a reflection of the former Moorish liking for those of the ostrich in their houses of worship.

To return for a moment to the notion that the ostrich breaks any eggs that become addled (by the way, how could the bird know which were "gone bad"?), let me add a preposterous variation of this, quoted from a German source by Goldsmith [32] in relation to the rhea, the South American cousin of the ostrich—all, of course, arrant nonsense:

> The male compels twenty or more females to lay their eggs in one nest; he then, when they have done laying, chases them away and places himself upon the eggs; however, he takes the singular precaution of laying two of the number aside, which he does not sit upon. When the young one comes forth these two eggs are addled; which the male having foreseen, breaks one and then the other, upon which multitudes of flies are found to settle; and these supply the young brood with a sufficiency of provision till they are able to shift for themselves.

Another popular saying is: "I have the digestion of an ostrich!"

What does this mean? Ancient books went so far as to say that ostriches subsisted on iron alone, although they did not take the trouble to explain where in the desert they could obtain this vigorous diet. A picture in one of the Beast Books gives a recognizable sketch of the bird with a great key in its bill and near by a horse-

shoe for a second course. In heraldry, which is a
museum of antique notions, the ostrich, when used as a
bearing, is always depicted as holding in its mouth a
Passion-nail (emblem of the Church militant), or a horse-
shoe (reminder of knightly Prowess on horseback), or
a key (signifying religious and temporal power).

An amusing passage in Sir Thomas Browne's famous
book, *Common and Vulgar Errors* [33]—which is a queer
combination of sagacity, ignorance, superstition and
credulity—is his solemn argument against the belief
prevalent in his day (1605-82) that ostriches ate iron;
but he quotes his predecessors from Aristotle down to
show how many philosophers have given it credence without proof. The great misfortune of medieval thinkers
appears to have been that they were bound hand and foot
to the dead knowledge contained in ancient Greek and
Latin books—a sort of mental mortmain that blocked
any progress in science. They made of Aristotle,
especially, a sort of sacred fetish, whose statements and
conclusions must not be "checked" by any fresh observation or experiment. Browne was one of the first to ex-
hibit a little independence of judgment, and to suspect
that possibly, as Lowell puts it, "they didn't know everything down in Judee."

"As for Pliny," Sir Thomas informs us, "he saith
plainly that the ostrich concocteth whatever it eateth.
Now the Doctor acknowledgeth it eats iron: ergo, according to Pliny it concocts iron. Africandus tells us
that it devours iron. Farnelius is so far from extenua-
ting the matter that he plainly confirms it, and shows that
this concoction is performed by the nature of its whole
essence. As for Riolanus, his denial without ground we
regard not. Albertus speaks not of iron but of stones

which it swallows and excludes again without nutriment."

This is an excellent example of the way those old fellows considered a matter of fact as if it were one of opinion—as if the belief or non-belief of a bunch of ancients, who knew little or nothing of the subject, made a thing so or not so. Sir Thomas seems to have been struggling out of this fog of metaphysics and shyly squinting at the facts of nature; yet it is hard to follow his logic to the conclusion that the allegation of iron-eating and "concocting" (by which I suppose digestion is meant) is not true, but he was right. The poets, however, clung to the story. John Skelton (1460-1529) in his long poem *Phyllip Sparrow* writes of

> The estryge that wyll eate
> An horshowe so great
> In the stede of meate
> Such feruent heat
> His stomake doth freat [fret].

Ben Johnson makes one of his characters in *Every Man in his Humor* assure another, who declares he could eat the very sword-hilts for hunger, that this is evidence that he has good digestive power—"You have an ostrich's stomach." And in Shakespeare's *Henry VI* is the remark: "I'll make thee eat iron like an ostrich, and swallow my sword."

Readers of Goldsmith's *Animated Nature*,[32] published more than a century later (1774) as a popular book of instruction in natural history (about which he knew nothing by practical observation outside of an Irish county or two), learned that ostriches "will devour leather, hair, glass, stones, anything that is given them, but all metals lose a part of their weight and often the

extremities of the figure." That the people remembered
this is shown by the fact that zoölogical gardens have lost
many specimens of these birds, which seem to have a very
weak sense of taste, because of their swallowing copper
coins and other metallic objects fed to them by experi-
mental visitors, which they could neither assimilate nor
get rid of. It is quite likely that the bird's reputation for
living on iron was derived from similarly feeding the captive specimens kept for show in Rome and various Eastern cities, the fatal results of which were unnoticed by
the populace. The wild ostrich contents itself with taking into its gizzard a few small stones, perhaps picked
up and swallowed accidentally, which assist it in grinding
hard food, as is the habit of many ground-feeding fowls.
Much the same delusion exists with regard to the emeu.

If I were to repeat a tithe of the absurdities and
medical superstitions (or pure quackery) related of birds
in the "bestiaries," as the books of the later medieval period answering to our natural histories were named, the
reader would soon tire of my pages; but partly as a
sample, and partly because the pelican is not only
familiar in America but is constantly met in proverbs, in
heraldry, and in ecclesiastical art and legend, I think it
worth while to give some early explanations of the
curious notion expressed in the heraldic phrase "the
pelican in its piety." It stands for a very ancient misunderstanding of the action of a mother-pelican alighting on her nest, and opening her beak so that her young
ones may pick from her pouch the predigested fish she
offers them within it. As the interior of her mouth is
reddish, she appeared to some imaginative observer long
ago to display a bleeding breast at which her nestlings
were plucking. Now observe how, according to Hazlitt,[84]

that medieval nature-fakir, Philip de Thaum, who wrote
The Anglo-Norman Bestiary about 1120, embroiders his
ignorance to gratify the appetite of his age for marvels—
sensations, as we say nowadays—and so sell his book:

"Of such a nature it is," he says of the pelican, "when it comes
to its young birds, and they are great and handsome, and it
will fondle them, cover them with its wings; the little birds
are fierce, take to pecking it—desire to eat it and pick out its
two eyes; then it pecks and takes them, and slays them with
torment; and thereupon leaves them—leaves them lying dead—
then returns on the third day, is grieved to find them dead, and
makes such lamentation, when it sees its little birds dead, that
with its beak it strikes its body that the blood issues forth; the
blood goes dropping, and falls on its young birds—the blood
has such quality that by it they come to life——"

and so on, all in sober earnest. But he made a botch of
it, for earlier and better accounts show that the male
bird kills the youngsters because when they begin to grow
large they rebel at his control and provoke him; when the
mother returns she brings them to life by pouring over
them her blood. Moreover, there crept in a further cor-
ruption of the legend to the effect that the nestlings were
killed by snakes, as Drayton writes in his *Noah's Flood:*

> By them there sat the loving pellican
> Whose young ones, poison'd by the serpent's sting,
> With her own blood again to life doth bring.

St. Jerome seems to have had this version in mind
when he made the Christian application, saying that as
the pelican's young, "killed by serpents," were saved by
the mother's blood, so was the salvation by the Christ related to those dead in sin. This point is elaborated somewhat in my chapter on *Symbolism.*

Before I leave this bird I want to quote a lovely paragraph on pelican habits, far more modern than anything "medieval," for it is taken from the *Arctic Zoölogy* (1784) of Thomas Pennant, who was a good naturalist, but evidently a little credulous, although the first half of the quotation does not overstrain our faith. He is speaking of pelicans that he saw in Australia, and explains:

They feed upon fish, which they take sometimes by plunging from a great height in the air and seizing like the gannet; at other times they fish in concert, swimming in flocks, and forming a large circle in the great rivers which they gradually contract, beating the water with their wings and feet in order to drive the fish into the centre; which when they approach they open their vast mouths and fill their pouches with their prey, then incline their bills to empty the bag of the waters; after which they swim to shore and eat their booty in quiet. . . . It is said that when they make their nests in the dry deserts, they carry the water to their young in the vast pouches, and that the lions and beasts of prey come there to quench their thirst, sparing the young, the cause of this salutary provision. Possibly on this account the Egyptians style this bird the *camel of the river*—the Persians tacub, or water-carrier.

Now let us look at the Trochilus legend, and trace how an African plover became changed into an American hummingbird. The story, first published by Herodotus, that some sort of bird enters the mouth of a Nile crocodile dozing on the sand with its jaws open, and picks bits of food from the palate and teeth, apparently to the reptile's satisfaction, is not altogether untrue. The bird alluded to is the Egyptian plover, which closely resembles the common British lapwing; and there seems to be no doubt that something of the sort does really take place when crocodiles are lying with open mouth on the Nile bank, as they often do. This lapwing has a

tall, pointed crest standing up like a spur on the top of
its head, and this fact gives "point," in more senses than
one, to the extraordinary version of the Herodotus story
in one of the old plays, *The White Devil*, by John Web-
ster (1612), where an actor says:

"Stay, my lord! I'll tell you a tale. The crocodile, which
lives in the river Nilus, hath a worm breeds i' the teeth of 't,
which puts it to extreme anguish: a little bird, no bigger than
a wren, is barber-surgeon to this crocodile; flies into the jaws
of 't, picks out the worm, and brings present remedy. The fish,
glad of ease, but ingrateful to her that did it, that the bird may
not talk largely of her abroad for nonpayment, closeth her
chaps, intending to swallow her, and so put her to perpetual
silence. But nature, loathing such ingratitude, hath armed this
bird with a quill or prick on the head, top o' the which wounds
the crocodile i' the mouth, forceth her open her bloody prison,
and away flies the pretty tooth-picker from her cruel patient."

A most curious series of mistakes has arisen around
this matter. Linguists tell us that the common name
among the ancient Greeks for a plover was *trochilus*
(τροχίλος), and that this is the word used by Herodotus for
his crocodile-bird. But in certain passages of his *History of Animals* Aristotle uses this word to designate a
wren; it has been supposed that this was a copyist's error,
writing carelessly τροχίλος for 'ορχίλος, but it was repeated
by Pliny in recounting what Herodotus had related, and
this naturally led to the statement by some medieval com-
pilers that the crocodile's tooth-cleaner was a wren.
This, however, is not the limit of the confusion, for when
American hummingbirds became known in Europe, and
were placed by some naturalists of the 17th century in
the Linnæan genus (Trochilus) with the wrens, one
writer at least, Paul Lucas, 1774 (if Brewer's *Handbook*
may be trusted), asserted that the hummingbird as well

as the lapwing entered the jaws of Egyptian crocodiles—
and that he had seen them do it!

This curious tissue of right and wrong was still further embroidered by somebody's assertion that the
diminutive attendant's kindly purpose was "to pick from
the teeth a little insect" that greatly annoyed the huge
reptile.   Even Tom Moore knew no better than to write
in *Lalla Rookh* of

> The puny bird that dares with pleasing hum
> Within the crocodile's stretched jaws to come.

The full humor of this will be perceived by those who
remember that hummingbirds are exclusively American—
not Oriental.   Finally Linnæus confirmed all this mixture
of mistakes by fastening the name Trochilidæ on the
Hummingbird family.

Finally, John Josselyn, Gent., in his *Rarities of New
England,* calls our American chimney-swift a "troculus,"
and describes its nesting absurdly thus:

> The troculus—a small bird, black and white, no bigger than
> a swallow, the points of whose feathers are sharp, which they
> stick into the sides of the chymney (to rest themselves), their
> legs being exceedingly short) where they breed in nests made
> like a swallow's nest, but of a glewy substance; and which is
> not fastened to the chymney as a swallow's nest, but hangs
> down the chymney by a clew-like string a yard long.   They
> commonly have four or five young ones; and when they go
> away, which is much about the time that swallows used to de-
> part, they never fail to throw down one of their young birds
> into the room by way of gratitude.   I have more than once ob-
> served, that, against the ruin of the family, these birds will
> suddenly forsake the house, and come no more.

Another unfortunate but long-accepted designation in
systematic ornithology was attached by Linnæus to the

great bird of paradise in naming this species *Paradisea apoda* (footless); and it was done through an even worse misunderstanding than in the case of Trochilus—or else as a careless joke. It is true that at that time no perfect specimen had been seen in Europe; yet it is hard to understand Linné's act, for he could not have put more faith in the alleged natural footlessness of this bird than in the many other marvelous qualities ascribed to it. Wallace has recounted some of these myths in his *Malay Archipelago*:[35]

When the earliest European voyagers reached the Moluccas in search of cloves and nutmegs, they were presented with the dried skins of birds so strange and beautiful as to excite the admiration even of those wealth-seeking rovers. The Malay traders gave them the name of "manuk dewata," or God's birds; and the Portuguese, finding they had no feet or wings, and being unable to learn anything authentic about them, called them "passares de sol" or birds of the sun; while the learned Dutchmen, who wrote in Latin, called them avis paradeus or paradise-bird. Jan van Linschoten gives these names in 1598, and tells us that no one has seen these birds alive, for they live in the air, always turning toward the sun, and never lighting on the earth till they die; for they have neither feet nor wings, as he adds, may be seen by the birds carried to India, and sometimes to Holland, but being very costly they were rarely seen in Europe. More than a hundred years later Mr. William Fennel, who accompanied Dampier . . . saw specimens at Amboyna and was told that they came to Banda to eat nutmegs, which intoxicated them, and made them fall senseless, when they were killed by ants. [Tavernier explains that the ants ate away their legs—thus accounting for the footlessness.]

It is to this nutmeg dissipation that Tom Moore alludes in *Lalla Rookh*:

> Those golden birds that in the spice time drop
> About the gardens, drunk with that sweet fruit
> Whose scent has lured them o'er the summer flood.

The unromantic fact was that the natives of the Moluccas then, as now, after skilfully shooting with arrows or blow-guns and skinning the (male) birds, cut off the legs and dusky wings and folded the prepared skin about a stick run through the body and mouth, in which form "paradise-birds" continued to come to millinery markets in New York and London. A somewhat similar blunder in respect to swallows (or swifts?) has given us in the martlet, as a heraldic figure, a quaint perpetuation of an error in natural history. "Even at the present day," remarks Fox Davies,[111] speaking of England, "it is popularly believed that the swallow has no feet . . . at any rate the heraldic swallow is never represented with feet, the legs terminating with the feathers that cover the shank."

I do not know where Dryden got the information suggesting his comparison, in *Threnodia Augustalis,* "like birds of paradise that lived on mountain dew"; but the idea is as fanciful as the modern Malay fiction that this bird drops its egg, which bursts as it approaches the earth, releasing a fully developed young bird. Another account is that the hen lays her eggs on the back of her mate. Both theories are wild guesses in satisfaction of ignorance, for no one yet knows precisely the breeding-habits of these shy forest-birds, the females of which are rarely seen. Dryden may have read that in Mexico, as a Spanish traveller reported, hummingbirds live on dew; or he may have heard of the medieval notion that ravens were left to be nourished by the dews of heaven, and, with poetic license to disregard classification, transferred the feat to the fruit-eating birds of paradise.

Next comes that old yarn about geese that grow on trees. When or where it arose nobody knows, but somewhere in the Middle Ages, for Max Müller quotes a cardinal of the 11th century who represented the goslings as bursting, fully fledged, from fruit resembling apples. A century later (1187) Giraldus Cambrensis, an archdeacon reproving laxity among the priests in Ireland, condemns the practice of eating barnacle geese in Lent on the plea that they are fish; and soon afterward Innocent III forbade it by decree. Queer variants soon appeared. A legend relating to Ireland inscribed on a Genoese world-map, and described by Dr. Edward L. Stevenson in a publication of The Hispanic Society (New York) reads: "Certain of their trees bear fruit which, decaying within, produces a worm which, as it subsequently develops, becomes hairy and feathered, and, provided wings, flies like a bird."

An extensive clerical literature grew up in Europe in discussion of the ethics of this matter, for the monks liked good eating and their Lenten fare was miserably scanty, and a great variety of explanations of the alleged marine birth of these birds—ordinary geese (*Branta bernicla*) when mature—were contrived. That something of the kind was true nobody in authority denied down to the middle of the 17th century, when a German Jesuit, Gaspar Schott, was bold enough to declare that although the birth-place of this uncommon species of goose was unknown (it is now believed to breed in Spitzbergen and Nova Zembla), undoubtedly it was produced from incubated eggs like any other goose. Nevertheless the fable was reaffirmed in the *Philosophical Transactions* of the Scottish Royal Society for 1677. Henry Lee [36] recalls two versions of the absurd but prevalent theory. One is that certain trees, resembling willows, and growing always close to the sea, produced at the ends of their branches fruits in the shape of apples, each containing the embryo of a goose, which, when the fruit was ripe, fell into the water and flew away. The other is that the geese were bred from a fungus growing on rotten timber floating at sea, and were first developed in the form of worms in the substance of the wood.

It is plain that this fable sprang from the similitude to the wings of tiny birds of the feathery arms that sessile barnacles reach out from their shells to clutch from the water their microscopic food, and also to the remote likeness the naked heads and necks of young birds bear to stalked or "whale" barnacles (Lepas). Both these cirripeds are found attached to floating wood, and sometimes to tree-branches exposed to waves and to high tides. The deception so agreeable to hungry churchmen was abetted by the etymologies in the older dictionaries. Dr. Murray, editor of *The New Oxford Dictionary*, asserts, however, that the origin of the word "barnacle" is not known, but that certainly it was applied to the mature goose before its was given to the cirriped.

Speaking of geese, what is the probable source of the warning "Don't kill the goose that lays the golden eggs" beyond or behind the obvious moral of Æsop's familiar fable? The only light on the subject that has come to me is the following passage in Bayley's [24] somewhat esoteric book:

The Hindoos represent Brahma, the Breath of Life, as riding upon a goose, and the Egyptians symbolized Seb, the father of Osiris, as a goose. . . . According to the Hindoo theory of creation the Supreme Spirit laid a golden egg resplendent as the sun, and from the golden egg was born Brahma, the progenitor of the Universe. The Egyptians had a similar story, and described the sun as an egg laid by the primeval goose, in later times said to be a god. It is probable that our fairy tale of the goose that laid the golden egg is a relic of this very ancient mythology.

These notions in India probably were the seed of a Buddhist legend that comes a little nearer to our quest. According to this legend the Buddha (to be) was born a Brahmin, and after growing up was married and his wife bore him three daughters. After his death he was born again as a golden mallard (which is a duck), and determined to give his golden feathers one by one for the support of his former family. This beneficence went on, the mallard-Bodhisat helping at intervals by a gift of a feather. Then one day the mother proposed to pluck the bird clean, and, despite the protests of the daughters, did so. But at that instant the golden feathers ceased to be golden. His wings grew again, but they were plain white. It may be added that the Pali word for golden goose is *hansa*, whence the Latin *anser*, goose, German *gans*, the root, *gan* appearing in our words gander and gannet; so that it appears that the "mallard" was a goose, after all—and so was the woman!

This may not explain Æsop, for that fabulist told or wrote his moral anecdotes a thousand years before Buddhism was heard of; but it is permissible to suppose that so simple a lesson in bad management might have been taught in India ages before Æsop (several of whose fables have been found in early Egyptian papyri), and was only repeated, in a new dressing, by good Buddhists, as often happens with stories having a universal appeal to our sense of practical philosophy or of humor.

We have had occasion to speak of the eagle in many different aspects, as the elected king of the birds, as an emblem of empire, and so on, but there remain for use in this chapter some very curious attributes assigned to the great bird by ancient wonder-mongers that long ago would have been lost in the discarded rubbish of primitive ideas—mental toys of the childhood of the world—had they not been preserved for us in the undying pages of literature. Poetry, especially, is a sort of museum of antique inventions, preserving for us specimens—often without labels—of speculative stages in the early development of man's comprehension of nature.

In the case of the eagle (as a genus, in the Old World not always clearly distinguished from vultures and the larger hawks) it is sometimes difficult to say whether some of its legendary aspects are causes or effects of others. Was its solar quality, for example, a cause or a consequence of its supposed royalty in the bird tribe? The predatory power, lofty flight, and haughty yet noble mien of the true eagle, may account for both facts, together or separately. It would be diving too deeply into the murky depths of mythology to show full proof, but it may be accepted that everywhere, at least in the East, the fountain of superstitions, the eagle typified the sun in its divine aspect. This appears as a long-accepted conception at the very dawn of history among the sun-worshippers of the Euphrates Valley, and it persisted in art and theology until Christianity remodelled such "heathen" notions to suit the new trend of religious thought, and transformed the "bird of fire" into a symbol of the Omnipotent Spirit—an ascription which artists interpreted very liberally.

In Egypt a falcon replaced it in its religious significance, true eagles being rare along the Nile, and "eagle-hawks" were kept in the sun-gods' temples, sacred to Horus (represented with a hawk-head surmounted by a sun-disk), Ra, Osiris, Seku, and other solar divinities. "It was regarded," as Mr. Cook explains in *Zeus*, [37] "as the only bird that could look with unflinching gaze at the sun, being itself filled with sunlight, and eventually akin to fire." Later, people made it the sacred bird of Apollo, and Mithraic worshippers spoke of Helios as a hawk, but crude superstitions among the populace were mixed with this priestly reverence.

It was universally believed of the eagle, that, as an old writer said, "she can see into the great glowing sun"; few if any were aware that she could veil her eyes by drawing across the orbs that third eyelid which naturalists term the nictitating membrane. Hence arose that further belief, lasting well into the Middle Ages, that the mother-bird proved her young by forcing them to gaze upon the sun, and discarding those who shrank from the fiery test—"Like Eaglets bred to Soar, Gazing on Starrs at heaven's mysterious Pow'r," wrote an anonymous poet in 1652. "Before that her little ones be feathered," in the words of an old compiler of marvels quoted by Hulme, [38] "she will beat and strike them with her wings, and thereby force them to looke full against the sunbeams. Now if she sees any one of them to winke, or their eies to water at the raies of the sunne, she turns it with the head foremost out of the nest as a bastard."

How many who now read the 103d Psalm, or that fine figure of rhetoric in Milton's *Areopagitica,* could explain the full meaning of the comparison used? The passage referred to is that in which Milton exclaims: "Methinks I see in my mind a noble and puissant nation rousing herself like a strong man after sleep. . . . Methinks I see her renewing her mighty youth, and kindling her undazzled eyes at the sun." Milton evidently expected all his readers to appreciate the value of his simile—to know that eagles were credited with just this power of juvenescence. "When," in the words of an even older chronicler, "an eagle hathe darkness and dimness in een, and heavinesse in wings, against this disadvantage she is taught by kinde to seek a well of springing water, and then she flieth up into the aire as far as she may, till she be full hot by heat of the air and by travaille of flight, and so then by heat the pores being opened, and the feathers chafed, and she falleth sideingly into the well, and there the feathers be chaunged and the dimness of her een is wiped away and purged, and she taketh again her might and strength." Isn't that a finely constructed tale? Spencer thought so when he wrote:

> As eagle fresh out of the ocean wave,
> Where he hath left his plumes, all hoary gray,
> And decks himself with feathers, youthful, gay.

Margaret C. Walker [39] elaborates the legend in her excellent book, suggesting that it may have originated in contemplation of the great age to which eagles are supposed to live; but to my mind it grew out of the ancient symbolism that made the eagle represent the sun, which plunges into the western ocean every night, and rises, its youth renewed every morning.

"It is related," says Miss Walker, "that when this bird feels the season of youth is passing by, and when his young are still in the nest, he leaves the aging earth and soars toward the sun, the consumer of all that is harmful. Mounting upward to the third region of the air—the region of meteors—he circles and swings about under the great fiery ball in their midst, turning every feather to its scorching rays, then, with wings drawn back, like a meteor himself, he drops into some cold spring or into the ocean wave there to have the heat driven inward by the soul-searching chill of its waters. Then flying to his eyrie he nestles among his warm fledglings, till, starting into perspiration, he throws off his age with his feathers. That his rejuvenescence may be complete, as his sustenance must be of youth, he makes prey of his young, feeding on the nestlings that have warmed him. He is clothed anew and youth is again his."

Cruden's *Concordance*[51] to the Bible, first published in 1737, contains under "Eagle" a fine lot of old Semitic misinformation as to the habits of eagles, which Cruden gives his clerical readers apparently in complete faith and as profitable explanations of the biblical passages in which that bird is mentioned. Allow me to quote some of these as an addition to our collection, for I find them retained without comment in the latest edition of this otherwise admirable work:

It is said that when an eagle sees its young ones so well-grown, as to venture upon flying, it hovers over their nest, flutters with its wings, and excites them to imitate it, and take their flight, and when it sees them weary or fearful it takes them upon its back, and carries them so, that the fowlers cannot hurt the young without piercing through the body of the old one. . . . It is of great courage, so as to set on harts and great beasts. And has no less subtility in taking them; for having filled its wings with sand and dust, it sitteth on their horns, and by its wings shaketh it in their eyes, whereby they become an easy prey. . . . It goeth forth to prey about noon, when men are gone home from the fields.

It hath a little eye, but a very quick sight, and discerns its prey afar off, and beholds the sun with open eyes, Such of her young as through weakness of sight cannot behold the sun, it rejects as unnatural. It liveth long, nor dieth of age or sickness, say some, but of hunger, for by age its bill grows so hooked that it cannot feed. . . . It is said that it preserves its nest from poison, by having therein a precious stone, named Aetites (without which it is thought the eagle cannot lay her eggs . . .) and keepeth it clean by the frequent use of the herb maidenhair. Unless it be very hungry it devoureth not whole prey, but leaveth part of it for other birds, which follow. Its feathers, or quills, are said to consume other quills that lie near them. Between the eagle and dragon there is constant enmity, the eagle seeking to kill it, and the dragon breaks all the eagle's eggs it can find.

If the Jewish eagles are as smart as that, my sympathies are with the dragon!

The relations between Zeus, or Jupiter, and the eagle, mostly reprehensible, belong to classic mythology; and they have left little trace in folklore, which, be it remembered, takes account of living or supposed realities, not of mythical creatures. The most notable bit, perhaps, is the widely accepted notion that this bird is never killed by lightning; is "secure from thunder and unharmed by Jove," as Dryden phrases it. Certain common poetic allusions explain themselves, for instance, that in *The Myrmidons* of Æschylus:

> So, in the Libyan fable it is told
> That once an eagle, stricken with a dart,
> Said, when he saw the fashion of the shaft,
> 'With our own feathers, not by others' hands
> 'Are we now smitten.'

These little narratives, which are certainly interesting if true—as they are not—are good examples of the failure to exercise what may be called the common-sense of science.

Extraordinary indeed are the foolish things that used to be told of birds by men apparently wise and observant in other, even kindred, matters. Isaak Walton,[40] for example, so well informed as to fish, seemed to swallow falsities about other animals as readily as did the gudgeon Isaak's bait. He writes in one place, after quoting some very mistaken remarks about grasshoppers,

that "this may be believed if we consider that when the
raven hath hatched her eggs she takes no further care,
but leaves her young ones to the care of the God of
Nature, who is said in the *Psalms* 'to feed the young
that call upon him.' And they be kept alive, and fed
by a dew, or worms that breed in their nests, or some
other ways that we mortals know not."

The origin of this is plain. The ancient Jews told one
another that ravens left their fledgings to survive by
chance, not feeding them as other birds did. This is
manifested in several places in the Bible, as in the 147th
Psalm: "He giveth to the beast his food *and* to the young
ravens which cry"; but this absurd notion is far older,
no doubt, than the Psalms. Aristotle [41] mentions that
in Scythia—a terra incognita where, in the minds of the
Greeks, anything might happen—"there is a kind of bird
as big as a bustard, which . . . does not sit upon its
eggs, but hides them in the skin of a hare or fox," and
then watches them from a neighboring perch. Readers
may guess at the reality, if any, behind this. Aristotle
seems to have accepted it as a fact, for he goes on to describe how certain birds of prey are equally devoid of
parental sense of duty; but we cannot be sure what species
are referred to, despite the names used in Cresswell's
translation of the *History of Animals,* as follows:

The bird called asprey . . . feeds both its young and those
of the eagle . . . for the eagle turns out its young . . . before
the proper time, when they still require feeding and are unable
to fly. The eagle appears to eject its young from the nest
from envy . . . and strikes them. When they are turned out
they begin to scream, and the phene comes and takes them up.

Why so strange notions of maternal care in birds
should ever have gained credence in the face of daily ob-

servation of the solicitude of every creature for its young, is one of the puzzles of history, but that they were wide-spread is certain, and also that they persisted in folklore down to the time when, at the dawn of the Renaissance, observation and research began to replace blind confidence in ancient lore. Thus J. E. Harting, [42] in his well-known treatise on the natural history in Shakespeare, quotes from a Latin folio of 1582 in support of his statement that "it was certainly a current belief in olden times that when the raven saw its young newly hatched, and covered with down, it conceived such an aversion that it forsook them, and did not return to its nest until a darker plumage showed itself."

Ravens have quite enough sins to answer for and calumnies to live down without adding to the list this murderous absurdity, contrary to the very first law of bird-nature. Nevertheless the poets, as usual, take advantage of the thought (for its moral picturesqueness, I suppose), as witness Burns's lines in *The Cotter's Saturday Night*—

> That he who stills the raven's clamorous nest
> .   .   .   .   .   .
> Would in the way his wisdom sees the best,
> For them and for their little ones provide.

It is plain that the plowman-poet was too canny to believe it, but perhaps it is well to say that there is no foundation in fact for this extraordinary charge. Ravens are faithful and careful parents: in fact Shakespeare makes a character in *Titus Andronicus* mention that "some say that ravens foster forlorn children," a view quite the opposite of the other.

Another calumny is thoughtlessly repeated by Brewer [34]

in his widely used reference-book *Phrase and Fable*
(which unfortunately is far from trustworthy in the department of natural history) when he records: "Ravens
by their acute sense of smell, discern the savor of dying
bodies, and under the hope of preying on them, light on
chimney-tops or flutter about sick-rooms."

The correction to be made here is not to the gruesome
superstition but to the asserted keenness of the bird's
sense of smell. The gathering of vultures to a dead
animal is not by its odor, but by the sight of the carcass
by one, and the noting of signs of that fact by others,
who hasten to investigate the matter. Oliver Goldsmith [32]
fell into the same error when he wrote of the protective
value, as he esteemed it, of this sense in birds in general,
"against their insidious enemies"; and cited the practice
of decoymen, formerly so numerous as wildfowl trappers
in the east of England, "who burn turf to hide their
scent from the ducks." The precaution was wasted, for
none of the senses in birds is so little developed or of
so small use as the olfactory. Goldsmith's *Animated
Nature* was, a century ago, the fountain of almost all
popular knowledge of natural history among English-
reading people, and was often reprinted. As a whole it
was a good and useful book, but its accomplished author
was not a trained naturalist, and absorbed some statements that were far from authentic—perhaps in some
cases he was so pleased with the narrative that he was not
sufficiently critical of its substance, as in the story of
the storks in Smyrna:

The inhabitants amuse themselves by taking away some of
the storks' eggs from the nests on their roofs, and replacing
them with fowls' eggs. "When the young are hatched the sagacious male bird discovers the difference of these from their own

brood and sets up a hideous screaming, which excites the attention of the neighboring storks, which fly to his nest. Seeing the
cause of their neighbor's uneasiness, they simultaneously com-
mence pecking the hen, and soon deprive her of life, supposing
these spurious young ones to be the produce of her conjugal
infidelity. The male bird in the meantime appears melancholy,
though he seems to conceive she justly merited her fate."

In Goldsmith's day such contributions to foreign
zoology were common. Even the so-called scientific men of
early Renaissance times indulged in the story-teller's joy.
Albertus Magnus asserted that the sea-eagle and the
osprey swam with one foot, which was webbed, and captured prey with the other that was armed with talons.
Aldrovandus backed him up, and everybody accepted the
statement until Linnæus laughed them out of it by the
simple process of examining the birds. These, you may
protest, are not mistakes but pure fancies; yet it is only
a short step from them to the romance, hardly yet under
popular doubt, that the albatross broods its eggs in a raft-
like, floating nest and sleeps on the wing, as you may
read in *Lalla Rookh:*

> While on a peak that braved the sky
> A ruined temple tower'd so high
> That oft the sleeping albatross
> Struck the wild ruins with her wing,
> And from her cloud-rocked slumbering
> Started, to find man's dwelling there
> In her own fields of silent air.

Even more poetic is the tale of the death-chant of the
swan, still more than half-believed by most folks, for
we constantly use it as a figure of speech, describing in a
word, for example, the final protest of a discarded office-
seeker as his "swan-song." It is useless to hunt for the

origin of this notion—it was current at any rate in Aristotle's time, for he writes: "Swans have the power of
song, especially when near the end of their life, and some
persons, sailing near the coast of Libya, have met many
of them in the sea singing a mournful song and have
afterwards seen some of them die." Pliny, Ælian (who
called Greece "mother of lies"), Pausanias and other more
recent philosophers, denied that there was any truth in
this statement; but the sentimental public, charmed by the
pathos of the picture presented to their imaginations, and
refusing to believe that in reality this bird's only utterance
is a whoop, or a trumpet-like note, have kept it alive
aided by the poets who have found it a useful fancy—
for example Byron, who moans

> Place me on Sunium's marbled steep,
>   Where nothing save the waves and I
> May hear our mutual murmurs sweep;
>   There, swan-like, let me sing and die.

The poets are not to be quarrelled with too severely on
this account. It must be conceded that our literature
would have been considerably poorer had poets declined
to accept all that travellers and country folk told them.
Chaucer uses the "swan-song," and Shakespeare often
alludes to it, as in *Othello:*

> I will play the swan and die in music.
> A swan-like end, fading in music.

Even Tennyson has a poem on it, picturing a scene of the
most charming nature, the pensive beauty of which is
vastly enhanced by the bold use of the fable.

It has required both the hard scientific scrutiny of the
past century and a wide scattering of geographical infor-

mation, to offset in the minds of most of us the tendency to imagine that "over the hills and far away" things somehow are picturesquely different from those in our own humdrum neighborhood, and that perhaps *yonder* the laws of nature, so inexorable here, may admit now and then of exceptions. Amber came from—well, few persons knew precisely whence; and wasn't it possible that it *might* be a concretion of birds' tears, as some said?

> Around thee shall glisten the loveliest amber
> That ever the sorrowing sea-bird hath wept—

sang an enamored poet.

Facilis descensus Averni is a Latin phrase in constant use, with the implication that it is difficult to get back— *sed revocare gradus,* that's the rub! But how many know that this dark little cliff-ringed lake near Cumae, in Italy, was anciently so named in the belief that because of its noxious vapors no bird could fly across it without being suffocated. Hence a myth placed there an entrance to the nether world, and, with keen business instincts, the Cumaean sybil intensified her reputation as a seer by taking as her residence a grotto near this baleful bit of water.

Who can forget the monumental mistake of that really great and philosophic naturalist, Buffon, in denying that the voices of American birds were, or could be, melodious. He said of our exquisite songster, the wood-thrush, that it represented the song-thrush of Europe which had at sometime rambled around by the Northern Ocean and made its way into America; and that it had there, owing to a change of food and climate, so degenerated that its cry was now harsh and unpleasant, "as are the cries of all birds that live in wild countries inhabited by savages."

The danger of error in drawing inferences as to purpose in nature is great in any case; but it is doubly so when the philosopher is mistaken as to his supposed facts.

By going back a few decades one might find examples of more or less amusing errors in natural history to the point of weariness, but with one or two illustrations from *The Young Ladies' Book* (Boston, 1836), I will bring this chapter to its end. This little volume, doubtless English in origin, was intended for the entertaining instruction of school-girls, and in many respects was excellent, but when it ventured on American ornithology it put some amusing misinformation into its readers' minds. It teaches them that our butcherbirds "bait thorns with grasshoppers to decoy the lesser insectivorous birds into situations where they may easily be seized"—a beautiful sample of teleological assumption of motive based on the fact that the shrike sometimes impales dead grasshoppers, mice and so forth on thorns or fence-splinters, having learned apparently that that is a good way to hold its prey (its feet are weak, and unprovided with talons) while it tears away mouthfuls of flesh. Often the victim is left there, only partly eaten, or perhaps untorn; and rarely, if ever, does the shrike return to it, and certainly it attracts no "lesser insectivorous" birds nor any other kind.

The author also instructs his young ladies that "the great American bittern has the property of emitting a light from its breast," and so forth. His authority for this long-persistent and picturesque untruth was a review of Wilson's *American Ornithology* in Loudon's *Magazine of Natural History* (London, Vol. vi., 835.) Speaking of this familiar marsh-bird, which, let me repeat, has no such aid in making a living, or need of it, as it is not nocturnal in its habits, the anonymous reviewer writes:

It is called by Wilson the great American bittern, but, what is very extraordinary, he omits to mention that it has the power of emitting a light from its breast, equal to the light of a common torch, which illuminates the water so as to enable it to discover its prey. . . . I took some trouble to ascertain the truth of this, which has been confirmed to me by several gentlemen of undoubted veracity, and especially by Mr. Franklin Peale, the proprietor of the Philadelphia Museum.

A similar belief existed in the past in regard to the osprey, which we in the United States call the fish-hawk. Loskiel (*Mission to the Indians,* 1794) records it thus: "They say that when it [the fish-hawk] hovers over the water, it possesses a power of alluring the fish toward the surface, by means of an oily substance contained in its body. So much is certain, that, if a bait is touched with this oil, the fish bite so greedily, that it appears as if it were impossible for them to resist." How much of this is native American, and how much is imported it is hard to determine now.

CHAPTER IV

THE FOLKLORE OF BIRD MIGRATION

I WAS sitting on a hillside in the Catskill Mountains a few years ago in June, when a hawk came sailing over the field below me. Instantly a kingbird sprang from the edge of the woods and rushed, in the cavalier manner of that flycatcher, to drive the hawk away, presumably from its nesting neighborhood. The hawk tried to avoid the pecking and wing-beating of its furious little foe, but the tormenter kept at it; and before long I saw the kingbird deliberately leap upward and alight on the hawk's broad back, where it rode comfortably until both birds were out of sight. I have seen a hummingbird indulge in the same piece of impudence.

The Arawak Indians of Venezuela relate that their ancestors obtained their first tobacco-plants from Trinidad by sending a hummingbird, mounted on a crane, to snatch and bring back the jealously guarded seeds. The association of these birds in this way seems significant.

It was doubtless because adventures similar to that of the kingbird were noticed long ago, that there grew up the very ancient fable that on one occasion a general assembly of birds resolved to chose for their king that bird which could mount highest into the air. This the eagle apparently did, and all were ready to accept his rule when a loud burst of song was heard, and perched upon the eagle's back was seen an exultant wren that, a stowaway under its wing, had been carried aloft by the kingly candidate. This trickiness angered the eagle so much, says one tradition, that he struck the wren with his wing, which, since then, has been able to fly no higher than a hawthorn-bush. In a German version a stork, not an eagle, carries the wren aloft concealed under its wing.

W. H. Hudson, the authority on Argentine zoology, says that the boat-tailed grakle, or "chopi," pursues all sorts of predatory birds, even the great caracara eagle, "pouncing down and fastening itself on the victim's back, where it holds its place till the obnoxious bird has left its territory." Sir Samuel Baker encountered in Abyssinia bands of cranes walking about in search of grasshoppers, every crane carrying on its back one or more small flycatchers that from time to time would fly down, seize an insect in the grass, and then return to a crane's shoulders. Precisely the same thing has been recorded of bustards and starlings in South Africa.

Bird-students are well aware that certain ducks that nest in trees, and such marine birds as guillemots breeding on sea-fronting cliffs, sometimes carry down their young from these lofty birth-places by balancing them on their backs; also that it is a common thing to see water-fowls, especially grebes and swans, swimming about with a lot of little ones on deck, that is, on the broad maternal back.

These facts prepare us somewhat for examining the widely credited assertion that various large birds of powerful flight transport small birds on their semiannual migrations—a speculation accepted since classic times, or before them. In *Deuteronomy*, xxxii, 11, we read: "As the eagle fluttereth over her young, spreadeth abroad her wings, taketh them, beareth them on her wings," etc.

Modern ornithologists scout the notion. Thus Alfred Newton [55] refers to it in a scornful way, but admits that it is the conviction not only of Egyptian peasants but of Siberian Tartars, who assured the ornithologist Gmelin, in 1740, that in autumn storks and cranes carried southward on their backs all the Siberian corncrakes. In a Gaelic folk-tale of Cathal O'Couchan a falcon, knowing that the wren of the story has a long way to go, says: "Spring up between my wings, and no other bird will touch thee till thou reach home."

In fact, this popular notion is almost world-wide, and it is useful to assemble such evidence as may be had as to the basis of it, for one cannot well dismiss with a gesture of disdain a theory that appears to have arisen independently, and from observation, among peoples so widely separated as those of Siberia and Egypt, of Crete and the Hudson Bay country; and which continues to be held by competent observers. A German man of letters, Adolph Ebeling, who published a book of his experiences in Egypt in 1878, was surprised to find the wagtail there at that season. This is a small, ground-keeping bird that flits about rather than flies; and he expressed to an old Arab his astonishment that such birds should be able to get across the Mediterranean. "The Bedouin," Ebeling relates, "turned to me with a mixture of French and Arabic as follows: 'Do you not know, noble sir, that these small birds are borne over the sea by the larger ones?'"

I laughed, but the old man continued quite naturally:

"Every child among us knows that. Those little birds are much too weak to make the long sea-journey with their own strength. This they know very well, and therefore wait for the storks and cranes and other large birds, and settle themselves upon their backs. In this way they allow themselves to be borne over the sea. The large birds submit to it willingly, for they like their little guests who by their merry twitterings help to kill the time on the long voyage."

Ebeling met that evening, he says, in Cairo, the African explorer Theodor von Heuglin, who, as all know, was a specialist in African ornithology, related to him the conversation with the Bedouin, and asked his opinion on it. "Let others laugh," said von Heuglin. "I do not laugh, for the thing is known to me. I should have recently made mention of it in my work if I had had any strong personal proof to justify it. We must be much more careful in such matters than a mere story-teller or novelist."

A Swedish traveller, Hedenborg, is quoted by August Petermann, the geographer, as stating that in autumn on the Island of Rhodes, in the Ægean Sea, when the storks came in flocks across the water he often heard birds singing that he was unable to discover. "Once he followed a flock of storks, and as they alighted he saw small birds fly up from their backs."

There was published in London in 1875 a book entitled *Bible Lands and Bible Customs,* the author of which was the Rev. Henry J. Van Lennep, D.D. Dr. Lennep informs his readers that many small birds are unable to fly across the Mediterranean, "and to meet such cases the crane has been provided. . . . In the autumn numerous flocks may be seen coming from the north . . . flying low and circling over the plains. Little birds of various species may then be seen flying up to them, while the twittering songs of those comfortably settled on their backs may then be distinctly heard." (Quoted in *Nature,* March 24, 1881). We may smile at the good man's faith

that God "provided" big birds as carriers for little ones—
especially as we know that the weakest warblers are able
to cross from Europe to Africa; but other equally modern
and more matter-of-fact testimony comes from the same
quarter of the world. In *The Evening Post,* of New
York City, dated November 20, 1880, a long letter appeared on this topic, written by an anonymous corre-
spondent who gave his own similar experience in Crete
in the autumn of 1878, part of which reads:

"On several occasions the village priest—a friendly Greek
with whom I spent the greater part of my time—directed my
attention to the twittering and singing of small birds which he
distinctly heard when a flock of sand-cranes passed by on
their southward journey. I told my friend that I could not see
any small birds, and suggested that the noise came from the
wings of the large ones. This he denied, saying 'No, no! I
know it is the chirping of small birds. They are on the backs
of the cranes. I have seen them frequently fly up and alight
again, and they are always with them when they stop to rest and
feed.' I was still sceptical, for with the aid of a field-glass I
failed to discover the 'small birds' spoken of. I inquired of
several others and found the existence of these little feathered
companions to be a matter of general belief. 'They come over
from Europe with them.' One day, while fishing about fifteen
miles from shore, a flock of cranes passed quite near the yacht.
The fishermen, hearing the 'small birds,' drew my attention to
their chirping. Presently one cried out, 'There's one!' but I
failed to catch sight of it, whereupon one of the men discharged
his flintlock. Three small birds rose up from the flock and soon
disappeared among the cranes."

This letter, despite its column-length and its anonym-
ity, was copied in full by that highly scientific journal
Nature, of London, and this immediately brought out a
note from John Rae, one of the wisest explorers of northwestern Canada, who related (*Nature,* March 3, 1881)
that it was the general belief among the Maskegan (Cree)

Indians dwelling along the southwestern shore of Hudson Bay that "a small bird, one of the Fringillidae, performs its northward migration in spring on the back of the Canada goose. These geese reach Hudson Bay about the last of April, and the Indians state that when they are fired at little birds are seen flying away from them." Mr. Rae adds: "An intelligent, truthful and educated Indian, named George Rivers . . . assured me that he had witnessed this, and I believe I once saw it occur."

Almost simultaneously *Forest and Stream* (New York, March 10, 1881) printed a communication from J. C. Merrill of Fort Custer, Montana, alleging "a general belief among the Crow Indians of Montana that the sandhill crane performs the same office for a bird they call *napite-shu-utl*, or crane's back." Mr. Merrill continued:

"This bird I have not seen, but from the description it is probably a small grebe. It is 'big medicine,' and when obtained is rudely stuffed and carefully preserved. . . . About ten or fifteen per cent of cranes are accompanied by the 'crane-back,' which, as the crane rises from the ground, flutters up and settles on the back between the wings, remaining there until the crane alights. Such is the Indian account, and many of their hunters and chiefs have assured me that they have frequently seen the birds carried off in this way. At these times the bird is said to keep up a constant chattering whistle, which is the origin of the custom of the Crow warriors going out to battle, each with a small bone whistle in his mouth; this is continually blown, imitating the notes of the 'crane's-back,' and, as they believe, preserves their ponies and themselves from wounds, so that in case of defeat they may be safely carried away as is the napite-shu-utl.

"The Cree Indians are said to observe the same habit in the white crane."

Now there is no good reason to deny the honesty or sneer at the value of these widely distributed observations so long as they are regarded as descriptive of exceptions and not of a rule of migration. Neither the observers nor the reporters had any motive for deception, and are not likely to deceive themselves in every case—moreover, new witnesses continually arise. For example: Mr. E. Hagland, of Therien, Alberta, wrote to me as follows in a casual way, without any prompting, in April, 1919:

"One fall a flock of cranes passed over me flying very low, and apart from their squawking I could distinctly hear the twittering of small birds, sparrows of some kind. The chirping grew louder as the cranes drew towards me, and grew fainter as they drew away; and as the cranes were the only birds in sight I concluded that little birds were taking a free ride to the south."

The manner of flight of sandhill cranes as described by Dr. Elliott Coues [50] suggests why they might well be utilized as common carriers by small birds going their way. "Such ponderous bodies, moving with slowly beating wings, give a great idea of momentum from mere weight . . . for they plod along heavily, seeming to need every inch of their ample wings to sustain themselves." This would make it easy and tempting for a tired little migrant to rest its feet on the crane's broad back—and once settled there, why not stay?

The flaw in this whole matter is the unwarranted inference made by the Bedouins who talked with Herr Ebling, and by wiser persons, namely, that *all* the wagtails and other little birds annually perform their overseas journeys by aid of stronger-winged friends. That is reasoning from some to all, which is bad logic. It is as if a stranger in town noticed a few schoolboys hopping on the back of a wagon, and immediately noted down that in Pequaket boys in general rode to school on the tailboards of farm-wagons. Little birds, like small boys, have sense enough in their migrations to utilize a convenience when it is going their way—in other words a very few lucky ones each year manage to "steal a ride."

Thus far we have been dealing with a matter pretty close to actual ornithology; but it is only within recent years that study has made clear to us "the way of an eagle in the air," which, as a symbol of the semiannual movement of bird-hosts, was such a mystery to our forefathers. They imagined many quaint explanations, often no more sensible than the theory of the Ojibway Indians, who say that once bird-folk played ball with the North Wind. The latter won the game, and those kinds of birds who were on his side now stay in the North all winter, while those of the defeated side are obliged to flee southward every autumn, as their ancestors did at the end of the great ball-game.

Sir Walter Scott recalls in one of his novels the fond conceit of the little nuns in the abbey of Whitby, on the Northumberland coast, that the wee immigrants arriving there after their flight across the North Sea fluttered to earth not in weariness of wings but to do homage to Hilda, their saintly abbess. That was fifteen long centuries ago; but the story is true, for you may still see the ruins, at least, of Hilda's abbey, and still, spring by spring, do tired birds pause beside it as if to pay their devotions.

Much less pleasant is the dread inspired in the hearts of those who listen to the Seven Whistlers. Formerly no Leicestershire miner would go down into a pit, after hearing them, until a little time had elapsed, taking the sounds as a warning that an accident was impending; and doubtless coincident mishaps occurred often enough to confirm faith in the presentiment. Level-headed men knew well enough what the Seven Whistlers were—"it's them long-billed curlews, but I never likes to hear 'em," said one. The northern name of these birds is "whimbrel," a form of the English *whimperer*. As these curlews when migrating often travel low on dark nights, and are unseen, it is not strange that their unearthly cries should chill the imagination of the superstitious, and that the Scotch should call them "corpse-hounds." "Gabble retchet" is another Scotch term; and probably the Irish banshee had a similar origin. Still another name is "Gabriel hounds," originating, it is thought in Scandinavia, and explained by the fact that there the calling to one another of bean-geese in their nocturnal journeys, in spring, have a singular resemblance to the yelping of beagles; and the story is that Gabriel is obliged to follow his spectral pack, said to be human-headed, high in the dark air, as a punishment for having once hunted on Sunday.

Wordsworth in one of his sonnets connects this belief with the German legend of the Wild Huntsman, "doomed the flying hart to chase forever on aërial grounds." A Lancashire explanation, quoted by Moncure D. Conway is that these migrants, there deemed to be plovers, were "Wandering Jews," so called because they contained the souls of Jews who assisted at the Crucifixion, and in consequence were condemned to float in the air forever. A curious coincidence, given by Skeat,[7] is that the Malays have an elaborate story of a spectral huntsman, and hear him in the nocturnal notes of the birikbirik, a nightjar.

It is hardly more than a century ago that intelligent men abandoned the belief that certain birds hibernated in hollow trees, caverns, or even buried themselves every autumn in the mud at the bottom of ponds, and then recovered in the spring. This theory is of great antiquity, and was applied especially to the swallows, swifts, nightingales and corncrakes of the Mediterranean region; but even Aristotle doubted whether it was true of all birds. He discusses at some length in his *Natural History* [41] the winter retreat of fishes and other creatures that hibernate, and continues:

"Many kinds of birds also conceal themselves, and they do not all, as some suppose, migrate to warmer climes . . . and many swallows have been seen in hollow places almost stripped of feathers; and kites, when they first showed themselves, have come from similar situations. . . . Some of the doves conceal themselves; others do not, but migrate along with the swallows. The thrush and the starling also conceal themselves."

I have an unverified memorandum from the pen of Antonio Galvano, who resided in Mexico, long ago, that in his time hummingbirds "live of the dew, and the juyce of flowers and roses. They die or sleeepe every yeere in the moneth of October, sitting upon a little bough in a warme and close place: they revive or wake againe in the moneth of April after that the flowers be sprung, and therefore they call them the revived birds."

Even Gilbert White,[45] was inclined to think hibernation might be true, at least of British swallows; and Cowper sings—

> The swallows in their torpid state
> Compose their useless wings.

Alexander Wilson [46] thought it necessary to combat vigorously the same fiction then persistent among Pennsylvania farmers, and did so at length in his *American Ornithology* published in 1808.

But the wildest hypothesis was the one prevalent in the

Middle Ages and alluded to by Dryden in his poem *The
Hind and The Panther,* speaking of young swallows in
autumn:

> They try their fluttering wings and trust themselves in air,
> But whether upward to the moon they go,
> Or dream the winter out in caves below,
> Or hawk for flies elsewhere, concerns us not to know.
> Southwards, you may be sure, they bent their flight,
> And harbored in a hollow rock by night.

Or as Gay's shepherd surmises: [8]

> He sung where woodcocks in the summer feed,
> And in what climates they renew their breed;
> Some think to northern coasts their flight tend,
> Or to the moon in midnight hours ascend:
> When swallows in the winter season keep,
> And how the drowsy bat and dormouse sleep.

A quaint theological justification of this theory that
birds fly to the moon as a winter-resort is to be found in
Volume VI of *The Harleian Miscellany.* It is entitled
"An Inquiry into the Physical and Literal Sense of the
Scriptures," and is an exegesis of Jeremiah viii, 7: "The
stork in the heaven knoweth her appointed time, and the
turtle and the crane and the swallow observe the time
of their coming." The reverend commentator, whose
name is lost, begins at once to explain migration among
birds. He first assures his readers that many birds, including storks, often fly on migration at a height that
renders them indiscernible. Now, he argues, if the flight
of storks had been in a horizontal direction flocks of
birds would have been seen frequently by travellers—
ignoring the fact that they are and always have been observed. But, he goes on, as the flight is not horizontal it

must be perpendicular to the surface of the earth, and,
therefore, it becomes clear that the moon would be the
first resting-place the birds would be likely to strike,
whereupon he draws this conclusion: "Therefore the
stork, and the same may be said of other season-observing
birds, till some place more fit can be assigned to them, does
go unto, and remain in some one of the celestial bodies;
and that must be the moon, which is most likely because
nearest, and bearing most relation to this our earth, as
appears in the Copernican scheme; yet is the distance
great enough to denominate the passage thither an itine-
ration or journey."

The author next clinches the matter by taking the
time that the stork is absent from its nesting-place, and
showing how it is utilized. Two months are occupied in
the upward flight, three for rest and refreshment, and
two more for the return passage. Thus this ingenious
writer lays what he considers a solid scientific foundation
beneath an ancient and vague theory.

The sudden vanishing of some migratory birds while
others resembling them remained in view gave to ancient
ignorance—not yet altogether dissipated, even in these
United States—the belief that a bird might change into
the form of another. The difference noticed in plumage
in some species in summer and winter was accounted for
in the same way, as many old Greek myths illustrate.
Thus Sophocles, trying in one of his dramas to explain
an inconsistency between two versions of the myth of
Tereus, declares that the hoopoe of the older story is the
hawk of the newer one—the birds were altered, not the
narrative. He was easily believed, for to the Greeks of
his day it appeared plain that birds might become transformed into others birds. Aristotle took great pains to

show the absurdity of this notion, yet it has held on. Swann tells of an Englishman who declared that it was well-known that sparrow-hawks changed into cuckoos in spring; and another old belief is that the European land-rail becomes in winter the water-rail, resuming its own form in spring. A French name for the land-rail, by the way, is "king of the quails," because the quails chose it as leader in their migrations.

One of the most picturesque incidents in the story of the wilderness-roving of the Children of Israel, who were "murmuring" for the fleshpots of Egypt, is the sudden coming of quails that "filled the camp." The interpretation is plain that a migratory host of these birds had settled for the night where the Hebrews, or some of them, were; and the notable point is their abundance, and that they had disappeared when morning came, which is characteristic. These quails visit Europe in summer in prodigious numbers from south of the Mediterranean, and are netted for market by tens of thousands. It is said that in old times the bishops of Capri—Italy receives the greatest flight—derived a large part of their wealth from a tax on the catching of quails. Pliny alleges, as an example of the immense migrations of these quails in his time, that often, always at night, they settled on the sails of ships and so sank them. This really seems possible when one thinks of the small size of the "ships" of that period, and recalls that flights of our own migrating pigeons (now extinct) used to smash down stout branches of trees by the weight of the crowds of birds that settled on them.

Cranes are birds of striking characteristics, as we have seen, and seem to have impressed very forcibly the ancient Greeks as well as recent Orientals, the latter finding in

them an extraordinary symbolism.   The Greeks believed
that during their winter absence the cranes were in constant battle with the Pygmies—"That small infantry
warred on by cranes," as Milton characterized those
diminutive, but pugnacious folks who lived no one knew
exactly where, but certainly at the ends of the earth.
"The cranes travel," Aristotle records, "from Scythia to
the marshes in the higher parts of Egypt from which the
Nile originates.   This is the place where the Pygmies
dwell; and this is no fable, for there is really, it is said,
a race of dwarfs, both men and horses, which lead the
life of troglodytes."

> When the shrill clouds of Cranes do give alarmes,
> The valiant *Pigmy* stands unto his armes:
> Straight, too weak for the *Thracian* bird, he's swept,
> And through the eye in crooked tallons rapt.[48]

But this is only one item in the crane's list of wonders.
When this bird migrates it always flies against the wind,
according to ancient bird-minders, and carries a
swallowed stone as ballast so that it may not be swept out
of its course by a change of wind; and this stone when
it is vomited up is useful as a touchstone for gold.   Aristotle had heard of this ballasting precaution, and ex-
pressly denies it, but he says nothing about other stones
associated with the history of the bird, perhaps because
they had not been discovered in his day.   The sagacious
cranes were also said to post sentinels, while halting at
night, and to insure their necessary vigilance these sentinels were required to stand on one foot, and to hold in
the other, uplifted one a large stone.   Should one of
these sentinel-birds drowse the stone would drop and by
its noise awaken the sleepy sentry.   This explains the
fact that in British heraldry the crane is always repre-

sented with a bit of rock in its fist, the pose signifying
"vigilance."

Lyly,[49] in that queer old book *Euphues,* confesses:
"What I have done was only to keep myselfe from sleepe,
as the Crane doth the Stone in her foote; and I would
also, with the same Crane, that I had been silent, holding
a Stone in my mouth." His 16th-century readers understood this second simile, for they remembered that cranes
were said to be thus gagged when migrating, so as not
to utter any cries that would bring eagles or other birds of
prey to attack them.

This, perhaps, will be the most appropriate place to
mention some other quaint but widely credited stories of
birds possessed of stones, although they are not usually
connected with migratory habits.

The people of Rome in the old days were told of a
crystalline stone called *alectorius,* as large as a bean, to
be found in the gizzard of the barnyard cock. It was
held to have wonderful properties, endowing its possessor
with strength, courage, and success with women and
money, and to this apparently complete list of virtues is
added by one historian the quality of invisibility. This
last virtue also pertained to the stone placed by the raven
in the throat of its fledging, but the formalities described
as necessary for anyone who sought to obtain it were
quite impossible to fulfil. "It may, indeed," as Hulme [38]
remarks, "have had the same effect on the original owner,
as there could scarcely be an authentic instance of such
peculiar property being found." On the other hand we
are told that a stone from the hoopoe, when laid upon the
breast of a sleeping man, forced him to reveal any
rogueries he might have committed.

It is stated in Cassell's *Natural History* (Vol. IV),

that in India exists a popular superstition that if you will split the head of an adjutant stork before death you may extract from the skull "the celebrated stone called *zahir mora,* or 'poison-killer,' of great virtue and repute as an antidote to all kinds of poison." One would suppose that all the adjutants in India would long ago have been exterminated, but in fact this is one of the most numerous of birds there—the scavenger of every village.

The common swallow was once believed to have two of these miraculous stones stowed away somewhere in its interior. One was red, and cured an invalid instantly: the other, a black one, brought good fortune. Also, it was reported, swallows found on a seabeach, by some sort of inspiration, a particular kind of stone which would restore sight to the blind; and it was to this legend that Longfellow alluded in *Evangeline—*

Seeking with eager eyes that wondrous stone which the swallow
Brings from the shore of the sea to restore the sight of her
fledglings.

Various birds also gave, or strengthened, sight to their young by means of certain plants mentioned by old herbalists. Finally, it should not be overlooked that on page 152 of the most recent edition of Cruden's celebrated *Concordance* [51] to the Bible, among the generally astonishing notes beneath the word "eagle" is printed the following: "It is said that it preserves its nest from poison, by having therein a precious stone, named Aetites (without which it is thought the eagle cannot lay her eggs, and which some use to prevent abortion and help delivery in women, by tying it above or below the navel) and keepeth it clean by the frequent use of the herb maiden-hair."

Now it is all well enough to find this information in the writings of Pliny senior, who alleges that these "eagle-stones" (in fact natural hollow nodules of iron-impreg-nated clay) were transported by nesting eagles to their domiciles to assist them in ovulation, whence by analogy—recognizing unwittingly the kinship of men and animals—they would aid women in travail, and to smile over it with the shrewd editor of *Vulgar Errors*,[33] but it is odd to find such an absurdity recommended by a modern clergyman as "profitable" material for sermons.

Let me round out this chapter with that recognition of bird-migration in the custom among the Vikings of the 8th and 9th centuries of saying as they embarked upon some raid upon the coasts south of them that they were "following the swan's path."

CHAPTER V

NOAH'S MESSENGERS

OUR first thought when we hear the word "deluge" is of Noah and his Ark, and the funny toy of our childhood rises to the mind's eye. In that childhood we had no doubt that the flood described in the first book of the Old Testament covered the whole globe. Now we know that the story is a Semitic tradition, perhaps nothing more than a sun-myth in origin, although the actual occurrence of some extraordinary inundation may have got mixed with it and localized it. In fact, the belief in an all-submerging deluge, or, in what is its equivalent—namely, a time when the world was a plain of water with no land above its quiet surface—is a part of the mythology or theology, or both, of many diverse peoples in both hemispheres; and almost always birds are prominently associated with its incidents and the ensuing separation of land from water.

A surprising number of persons of ordinary intelligence even now, and in this enlightened country, continue to regard beds of water-worn gravels, and the fossil shells, etc., seen in the rocks, as relics of the Noachian deluge, and "diluvian" and "antediluvian" are terms that hardly yet have disappeared from popular geology.

The earliest available accounts of such a deluge as the Noachian are engraved on clay tablets recovered from the ruins of Babylonia, and written 2000 or more years before the beginning of the Christian era. Several narratives have been deciphered, agreeing in the facts of a vast destruction by water in Mesopotamia, and of a relatively huge house-boat built by a chosen family for the preservation of themselves and an extensive collection of livestock. After floating about for seven days this Babylonian ship grounded on a submerged hill-top, and seven days later the patriarchal shipmaster sent out as explorers a dove, a swallow, and a raven. The dove and the swallow returned, the raven did not.

The close similarity between this and the Biblical account of Noah's voyage on a world of waters (which account appears to be a combination of two separate legends) leads to the opinion that the whole narrative is derived from some more ancient and widespread Oriental tradition; and there seems fair evidence that it does not describe any physical happening at all, but is a symbolical sun-myth, a hint of which is given, even in the Bible, by the incident of the rainbow. Let me quote the history in Genesis so far as it relates to our purpose:

"And it came to pass at the end of forty days that Noah opened the window of the ark which he had made: and he sent forth a raven which went forth to and fro until the waters were dried up from off the earth. Also he sent forth a dove from him, to see if the waters were abated from off the face of the ground. But the dove found no rest for the sole of her foot, and she returned unto him into the ark; for the waters were on the face of the whole earth. Then he put forth his hand and took her, and pulled her in unto him into the ark. And he stayed yet other seven days; and again he sent forth the dove out of the ark. And the dove came in unto him in the evening, and, lo, in her mouth was an olive-leaf plucked off: so Noah knew that the waters were abated from off the earth. And he stayed yet other seven days, and sent forth the dove, which returned not again unto him any more.

As to the choice of these particular birds out of Noah's

great aviary, it is well to remember that doves were sacred in ancient Babylonia to Ishtar, who, as the deified (female) personification of productiveness, co-existent with the (male) Sun-god, was sometimes designated as Mother-goddess, or even as "Mother Earth": so that it would be highly appropriate to send first a dove as a messenger to this incarnation of fruitful land. This falls in with Moncure D. Conway's suggestion [56] that the dove and raven were tribally "sacred" animals among the people affected by this Babylonian deluge. The choice of the swallow was natural, when one remembers its habit of flying long and far over bodies of water; and that the raven should not come back is in keeping with its character as much as is the quick return of the semi-domestic dove and swallow. Dr. Laufer [52] notes that St. Ambrose, in his treatise *De Noe et Arca,* devotes a whole chapter to the "crow's" impiety in not returning to the Ark. The Arabs, according to Keane, [14] even yet call this bird "raven of separation," meaning the separation of the water from the land at the close of the Flood. Another Arabic source, quoted by Baring-Gould from the medieval *Chronicle* of Abou-djafer Tábari, transmits traditional particulars that considerably extend the too-laconic Biblical log of the Ark. "When Noah had left the Ark," it relates, "he passed forty days on the mountain, till all the water had subsided into the sea. . . . Noah said to the raven, 'Go and place your foot on the earth, and see what is the depth of the water.' The raven departed, but having found a carcass it remained to devour it and did not return. Noah was provoked, and he cursed the raven, saying, 'May God make thee contemptible among men, and let carrion be thy food.' "

Johann von Herder, the poet and friend of Goethe,

either found or invented another story to account for the curse resting on the raven, which runs thus in the words of an old translator:

Anxiously did Noah look forth from his swimming ark, waiting to see the waters of the flood abate. Scarcely had the peaks of the highest mountains emerged from the waves, when he called all the fowls around him. "Who among you," said he, "will be the messenger to go forth and see whether the time of our deliverance is nigh?" The raven with much noise crowded hastily in before all the rest: he longed ardently for his favorite food. Scarcely was the window open, when he flew away and returned no more. The ungrateful bird forgot his errand and the interests of his benefactor—he hung at his carcass! But punishment did not delay. The air was yet filled with poisonous fog, and heavy vapors hung over the putrid corpses; these blinded his eyes and darkened his feathers. As a punishment for his forgetfulness, his memory as well as his sight became dim; even his own young he did not recognize; and he experienced towards them no feelings of parental joy.

Quoting again the Arab chronicler Abou-djafer Tábari: "After that Noah sent forth the dove. The dove departed, and without tarrying put her foot in the water. The water of the Flood scalded and pricked the legs of the dove. It was hot and briny and feathers would not grow on her legs any more, and the skin scaled off. Now, doves which have red and featherless legs are of the sort that Noah sent forth. The dove returning showed her legs to Noah, who said: 'May God render thee well pleasing to men.' For that reason the dove is dear to men's hearts."

Still another Arabic version, given by Gustav Weil, is that Noah blessed the dove, and since then she has borne a necklace of green feathers; but the raven he cursed, that its flight should be crooked—never direct like that of other birds. This is also a Jewish legend. A more mod-

ern addendum is that the magpie, one of the same group
of birds, was not permitted to enter the ark, but was
compelled to perch on the roof because it gabbled so in-
cessantly. A quaint 14th-century manuscript quoted by
Hulme [38] says of the raven's exit from the ark:

> Then opin Noe his window
> Let ut a rauen and forth he flew
> Dune and vp sought heare and thare
> A stede to sett upon somequar.
> Vpon the water sone he fand
> A drinkled best ther flotand
>   Of that flees was he so fain
>   To ship came he never again.

To this list of messengers medieval tradition added a
fourth—the kingfisher, which in Europe is blue-green
above and rich chestnut on the breast. At that time, however, it was a plain gray bird. This scout flew straight up
to heaven, in order to get a wide survey of the waters,
and went so near the sun that its breast was scorched to
its present tint and its back assumed the color of the sky
overhead. (This recalls Thoreau's saying that our bluebird carries the sky on its back and the earth on its
breast.)

Faith in a general flood long ago is shown by primitive
documents to have prevailed not only in Asia Minor and
eastward, but in Persia, India and Greece. It did not
prevail in Europe generally, nor in Africa. On the other
hand missionaries report traditions of it in Polynesia—
where, curiously, geographers find evidence of great sub-
sidences since the archipelagoes affected have been inhabited; and certainly it was a part of the mythical pre-
history of many tribes among the aborigines of North
America, where birds were often connected with the ad-

ventures of the few or solitary survivors by means of
whom the world was repeopled. Thus scores, perhaps
hundreds, of varying traditions and fables exist of the
creation of the earth out of a chaos of water, or of its
restoration after having been drowned in a universal
flood; and often it is hard to distinguish the creation-myth
from the deluge-tale.

The American story-material of this nature may be
divided into groups that would correspond roughly to the
various aboriginal language-stocks, betraying a family
likeness in each group, but showing tribal variations as a
rule connected with each particular tribal or mythical
"first man," or with the totemic ancestor.

The creation-legends, as such, do not concern us much.
They are of purely mythical, supernatural beings of
various sorts, descending from the sky or coming up out
of the underworld, and either finding a readymade earth
to dwell upon or else creating one by magic. Some
Southern darkies will tell you that the bluejay made the
earth. "When all de worl' was water he brung de fust
grit er dirt." The strangest conception of this kind is not
American but that of the Ainus of northern Japan, who
say that the earth originally was a sterile, cold, unin-
habitable and dreadful quagmire. The creator existed
aloft, however, and finally made and despatched a water-
wagtail to construct a place habitable for men. The bird
fluttered over the water-spaces, trampled the thin mud
and beat it down with its feet. Thus ground was
gradually hardened and elevated in spots, the water
steadily drained away and good soil was left. Hence the
Ainus hold the little wagtail in almost worshipful esteem.

Let us, however, restrict the inquiry to North America,
and to the deluge-story proper—that is, the destruction of

human life by water overwhelming a flourishing world, and the subsequent restoration.

The widely spread Algonkin stock has many such legends, in which one or several persons and animals survive by floating in a canoe or raft, and at their behest a beaver or a muskrat—the most natural agents—bring up from the bottom a little mud, which is expanded by magic into a new continent; but frequently birds do this service or otherwise help to form livable conditions. The Lenni Lenape (Delawares) had a tradition of a universal deluge in the far distant past, which Dr. Brinton [27] recounted as follows, assuring us that it is unmixed with any teaching by white missionaries: "The few people that survived had taken refuge on the back of a turtle who had reached so great an age that his shell was mossy, like the bank of a runlet. In this forlorn condition a loon flew that way, which they asked to dive and bring up land. He complied but found no bottom. Then he flew away and returned with a small quantity of earth in his bill. Guided by him, the turtle swam to a place where a spot of dry land was found. There the survivors settled and re-peopled the land."

Few legends explain how or why the flood occurred. The Ojibways, however, say that it was the result of the malice of an underground monster visualized as a huge serpent (recalling the earth-dragon of the Chinese), which throughout all their mythology is the antagonist of the good, constructive genius represented by their tribal hero Manabozho.

The Beaver Indians of the Mackenzie Valley offer a more materialistic and more picturesque explanation. They told George Keith, one of the fur-traders there a century ago, whose Letters are printed in Masson's collection of northern archives,[99] that the deluge resulted from the sudden melting of a snowfall so deep that tall trees were buried. This disastrous melting was produced by the release of the sun from a bug in which it had been hidden by sorcery. Then the sun flew away and began to shed its heat. There's a sun-myth for you!

In the resulting freshet so philosophically accounted for the few persons who had been left unburied in the world of snow fled toward a high mountain, but only a man and a woman reached it. On this mountain were gathered pairs of all the kinds of animals in the country. The flood persisted, and there was nothing to eat. Then the mallard, the little grebe, or hell-diver, and the buzzard (?) were sent to dive into the sea and try to find its bottom. All failed repeatedly, but the buzzard dived again a few days later, and came up with his bill full of earth, which showed that the flood was subsiding. Finally the waters drained away or dried up, but the soil had been so ruined by submergence that not even roots could be found to serve as food. When everybody was nearly starved, however, the human pair and the animals succeeded in finding the home of Raven, who lived far away, and from his stores they obtained food. Then a new world of life began.

The Cheyennes and the Arikarees say that at the height of the flood "a person" (masculine) was floating in the water with all sorts of aquatic birds swimming about him. He asked that one of them dive and get some earth. All tried it and failed until a small duck brought up a little mud in its beak and gave it to the man. He kneaded it with his fingers until it was dry, then made little piles of it on the surface of the water, which enlarged and coalesced into a wide plain.

The Chitimacha Indians of northern Lousiana used to relate that a great deluge came, whereupon the redheaded woodpecker went up to the sky and hung by his claws to escape drowning, but his tail hung down into the dirty water and was stained black, as you now see it. The Pimas and other tribes of Arizona tell similar stories of certain birds, one clan of Pueblo Indians putting it on the turkey. They say that a flood was produced by the god Baholi Konga to punish tribal wickedness. The good persons in the community escaped this punishment by means of the fact that Baholi Konga had clothed them in turkey-skins, enabling them to fly to the high mountains. They flew too low, however, and the tails of their dresses dragged in the water, the stain of which is still visible.

With one more and a rather pretty tale from the traditions of the Paiute Indians, whose home is in the region of the Grand Canyon of the Colorado, I must close this glance at aboriginal legends of a deluge here in America. These Indians relate that formerly the whole world was under water save the summit of Mt. Grant, on which existed a fire. It was the only fire in the universe, and it would have been extinguished when the wind blew hard and the waves were dashed against the peak had not the sage-hen settled down there and fanned away the water with her wings; but while doing this inestimable service to mankind the heat of the precious flame scorched her breast, and that accounts for its present blackness.

A curiously similar story, which illustrates the primitive savage's perception that obtaining fire was the most important, the first, thing to do in beginning or reconstituting a habitable world, appears in the folklore of the Arawaks of British Guiana, and may well be told among deluge myths. They assure you that the world was once engulfed in a flood that left exposed only a hilltop where grew some tall cocoanut palms. The heavenly leader, Sigu, conducted all the animals to this hill and made such as could go up the trees, while others were placed in a cave sealed water-tight with wax. (It was during that long, distressful waiting in the palm-tops that the howling-monkeys perfected the agonizing quality of their terrific voices.) Finally the waters subsided and the agami (the trumpeter, *Psophia crepitans*) ventured too soon upon the ground in search of food; thereupon hordes of starved ants, issuing from their half-drowned nests, swarmed upon its legs, then of respectable size, and so nearly devoured them that only the sticklike shanks now characteristic of the bird remained. Sigu rescued the unfortunate agami, and then with infinite trouble kindled a fire with a spark that the maroodie (or guan, a fellow-bird with the agami of South-American barnyards) had snapped up in mistake for a shining red insect. The guan tried to shift the blame for this sinful error upon the alligator but failed to do so, for his own guilt was betrayed by the glowing spark that had stuck in his throat, as one may see by looking at any guan to-day.

Another instance of the misfortunes of the trumpeter is related by Leo Miller [53] as he heard it among the Maquritari Indians who live on the headwaters of the Orinoco:

In the very beginning of things a trumpeter and a curassow [a near cousin of the guan] decided upon a matrimonial alliance, but domestic troubles soon broke out, and there was no possibility of a reconciliation; it was thereupon decided to lay the case before the gods who live on the summit of Mount Duida. The wise gods ordered them to fight it out. In the course of the combat that followed the curassow pushed the trumpeter into the fire, burning off the feathers of the latter's tail. The trumpeter promptly retaliated by pushing her mate into the fire, singeing his crest. Thereupon the gods decided that they should remain in this humiliating plight for the rest of their days, and so . . . the curassow wears a curled crest and the trumpeter has a very short tail.

I am tempted, in spite of my intention to stop here, to annex an elaborate and somewhat amusing creation-myth of the Yocut Indians of southern California, because it is both appropriate and picturesque. It is thus set down by Powers:[19]

Once there was a time when there was nothing in the world but water. About the place where Tulare Lake now is, there was a pole standing far up out of the water, and on this pole, perched a hawk and a crow . . . for many ages. At length they wearied of the lonesomeness, and they created the birds which prey on fish, such as the kingfisher, eagle, pelican, and others. Among them was a very small duck, which dived down to the bottom of the water, picked its beak full of mud, came up, died, and lay floating on the water. The hawk and crow then fell to work and gathered from the duck's beak the earth which it had brought up, and commenced making the mountains. They began at the place now known as Ta-hi-cha-pa Pass, and the hawk made the east range, while the crow made the west one. Little by little, as they dropped in the earth, the great mountains grew athwart the face of the waters pushing north. It was a work of many years, but finally they met at Mt. Shasta, and their labors were ended.

But behold, when they compared their mountains it was found that the crow's was a great deal the larger. Then the hawk said to the crow. "How did this happen, you rascal? I warrant you have been stealing the earth from my bill, and that is why your mountains are the biggest." It was a fact, and the crow laughed in his claws. Then the hawk went and got some Indian tobacco and chewed it and it made him exceedingly wise. So he took hold of the mountains and turned them around in a circle, putting his range in place of the crow's; and that is why the Sierra Nevada is larger than the Coast Range.

CHAPTER VI

BIRDS IN CHRISTIAN TRADITION AND FESTIVAL

THE crowing of a cock ushered in the momentous tragedy that closed the earthly career of Jesus of Nazareth. Jesus had told one of his disciples in the evening of the Passover, that "the cock shall not crow this day before that thou shalt twice deny that thou knowest me" (*Luke,* xxii, 34). Later that same night Jesus was arrested and taken into the house of the Jewish high priest, and when, one after another, three persons had identified Peter as one of the Disciples Peter each time denied it, "and immediately, while he yet spake, the cock crew."

Although the cock and his brood have had a part in Oriental and classical superstitions, ceremonies, and myths since these things began, it is probable that Jesus had in mind nothing more than the time of "cock-crowing," which among the Jews was a recognized name of the third watch of the night, beginning at three o'clock in the morning. Mark enumerates the four watch-divisions when he says: "Ye know not when the master of the house cometh, at even, or at midnight, or at the cock-crowing, or in the morning."

Out of this simple matter, a natural habit of the bird, the early Christians, with the avidity of zealots for inspired pegs on which to hang new devotions, set up many theories and customs. For instance, I find in the English

periodical *Nature Notes* (VI, 189) the following, translated from the *Treasury of Brunetti Latini,* a teacher of
Dante in the poet's youth: "By the song of the cock we
may know the hour of the night, and even as the cock
before it singeth beateth its body with its wings, so should
a man before he prays flagellate himself." To this added
a fourteenth-century chant, as follows:

> Cock at midnight croweth loud,
>   And in this delighteth:
> But before he crows, his sides
>   With his wings he smiteth:
> So the priest at midnight, when
>   Him from rest he raiseth,
> Firstly doeth penitence,
>   After that he praiseth.

Ratzel mentions that in Abyssinia cocks were often
placed in churches as living alarm-clocks. It is a tradition
that at the moment of the great Birth the cock crowed:
Christus natus est! Hence as early as the 4th century
arose the belief in its crowing always on Christmas
eve—a legend alluded to by Shakespeare:

> Some say that ever 'gainst that season comes
> Whereon our Saviour's birth is celebrated,
> The bird of dawning singeth all night long.

By a similar passage in *Hamlet,* where Bernardo,
Heraldo, and Marcellus are discussing the apparition of
the ghost of Hamlet's father, the reader learns of another ancient superstition:

> *Bern.* It was about to speak when the cock crew.
> *Her.* And then it started like a guilty thing
>   Upon a fearful summons. I have heard
>   The cock, that is the trumpet to the morn,

Doth with his lofty and shrill-sounding throat
Awake the god of day; and, at his warning,
Whether in sea or fire, in earth or air,
The extravagant and erring spirit hies
To his confine: and of the truth herein
This present object made probation.
Mar. It faded on the crowing of the cock.

Not only ghosts, but the Devil and all his powers of darkness, especially warlocks and witches, must disappear at Chanticleer's cheerful warning that daylight is at hand.

Domestic fowls had become common in Palestine at the time of Jesus, having been received long before from Persia. According to the *Mishna* Jews were prohibited from selling a white cock to the heathen because it was suitable for sacrifice, but if it were defective it became unsuitable. Cyrus Adler tells us that they used to cut off a toe, and so circumvent the prohibition. Says the Talmud: "There be three that be unyielding—Israel among the peoples, the dog among beasts, and the cock among birds" (Beca, 56).

No doubt it is true, as Mr. R. L. Gales pointed out a few years ago in the *National Review,* that the sacred mythology of the Nativity and Passion, which is far wider than my immediate use of it, sprang up when the minds of people constantly dwelt on the Faith in a spirit of devotion rather than of controversy. "It seems, too, that there was in the Christianity of the earlier ages something that we may perhaps call a pantheistic element, which has since disappeared."

Russians tell the story that while Christ was hanging on the cross the sparrows were maliciously chirping *Jif! jif!* that is, "He is living, He is living!" in order to urge the tormenters to fresh cruelties; but the swallows cried,

with opposite intent, *Umer! Umer!*" "Dead! Dead!"
Therefore the swallow is blessed, but the sparrow is
under a curse, and ever since that time it hops, because its
legs are tied together, for its sin, by invisible bonds.
Another story is that the sparrow was the bird that betrayed the hiding-place of Jesus in the Garden at Geth-
semane, whereas all other birds tried to entice away the
officers who were searching for him, especially the
swallow, whose erratic flight still shows that it is seeking
to find him.

The oystercatcher is still known among the Gaels of
northern Scotland as St. Bride's lad, says Seton Gordon
(*Nineteenth Century,* 1923, p. 420) from the fact that
when that saint first visited Long Island she carried an
oystercatcher in each hand; also, there is an old Gaelic
tradition that this bird covered Jesus with seaweed when
his enemies appeared in hot pursuit. The oystercatcher was
therefore blessed, and still shows, as it flies, the form of
a cross on its plumage.

A Spanish legend asserts that the owl was once the
sweetest of singers; but that, having been present when
Jesus died, from that moment it has shunned daylight,
and now only repeats in a harsh tone *Cruz! Cruz!*

Most of the legends of the Cross, so far as concern
birds, at least, seem to have arisen in Sweden. The
Swedes say, for example, that a swallow hovered over the
Crucifixion crying *Svale! Svale!* "Cheer up! Cheer up!"
and it is therefore called in their country the bird of con-
solation. 'A' similar story is current in Scandinavia of the
stork, which is said to have cried to the Redeemer, as it
flew about the Cross, *Styrket! Styrket!* "Strengthen ye."
In both cases there is a play on the Swedish names of
these birds; but they testify that the stork, now virtually

mute, formerly had a voice. In Sweden, where the red
crossbill is a familiar winter bird, arose the tradition that
its peculiarly crossed beak became twisted by its efforts
to pull the nails from Christ's hands and feet:

> Stained with blood and never tiring
>   With its beak it doth not cease,
> From the Cross 't would free the Saviour
>   Its creator's son release.
>
> And the Saviour speaks in mildness:
>   Blest be thou of all the good!
> Bear as token of this moment
>   Marks of blood and holy rood.

So Longfellow paraphrases Julius Mosen's little German
hymn.

The same loving service has been attributed to the red-
browed goldfinch of Europe in a legend current in Great
Britain—a story put into verse in *The Spectator*
(London, 1910) by Pamela Tenant, partly thus:

> Held in his slender beak the cruel thing,
> Still with his gentle might endeavoring
>   But to release it.
>
> Then as he strove, spake One—a dying space—
> 'Take, for thy pity, as a sign of grace,
> 'Semblance of this, my blood, upon thy face
>   'A living glory.'

The complaining love-note of the wood-pigeon has, in
the northwestern part of Europe, become the subject of a
well-adapted and pathetic myth, as Watters [57] denomi-
nates it in his entertaining *Birds of Ireland*. "It is said
that a dove perched in the neighborhood of the holy cross
when the Redeemer was expiring, and, wailing its notes
of sorrow, kept repeating the words 'Kyrie! Kyrie!'

[Kyrie eleison—Lord have mercy!] to alleviate the agony
of his dying moments."

Of all the legends connecting birds with this awful
scene those relating to the little robin-redbreast of Europe
are most familiar, for they have been celebrated in poems
that everyone reads. The story is that the robin, pitying
the pain of the cruel crown pressed on the Saviour's brow,
plucked away the sharpest of the thorns; and some say
that before that moment the bird was all gray, and was
bound to remain so until it had done something worthy
of its having a red breast. A forgotten writer, whose
lines have been preserved in an old volume of *Notes and
Queries,* tells the story thus:

> Bearing his cross, while Christ passed by forlorn,
> His Godlike forehead by the mock crown torn,
> A little bird took from that crown one thorn,
> To soothe the dear Redeemer's throbbing head.
> That bird did what she could; His blood, 't is said,
> Down-dropping dyed her tender bosom red.
> Since then no wanton boy disturbs her nest;
> Weasel nor wildcat will her young molest—
> All sacred deem that bird of ruddy breast.

The Spaniards, however, believe swallows—also "redbreasts" in their way—to be the birds that pulled the
thorns from Christ's crown—two thousand of them!

Another northern tradition is that the robin carries in
its beak daily a drop of water to those shut up in the
"burning lake," and that its breast is red because scorched
by the flames of Gehenna. This old Swedish legend gave
Whittier the inspiration for an exquisite poem:

> He brings cool dew in his little bill,
>   And lets it fall on the souls of sin;
> You can see the mark on his red breast still
>   Of fires that scorch as he drops it in.

Still another theory explains that its reddish front remains tinctured by the stain it received in trying to staunch the blood that flowed from the Redeemer's pierced side.

Almost all boys in Great Britain are, or used to be, collectors of birds' eggs, before bird-protecting societies and public enlightenment restricted their destructive enthusiasm; but the nest of the "ruddock" (robin) was rarely disturbed by the most careless of them, who, if undeterred by any soft sentiment, were frightened by the superstition that bad luck followed any such vandalism. Many maxims to this effect might be quoted, one of which, a proverb in Cornwall, runs:

> He that hurts robin or wren
> Will never prosper, boy or men.

In Essex they repeat to children a little ballad like this:

> The robin and the redbreast,
>   The robin and the wren;
> If ye take out o' their nest
>   Ye'll never thrive again.
>
> The robin and the redbreast,
>   The martin and the swallow;
> If ye touch one o' their eggs
>   Bad luck will follow.

The Scotch say it a little differently:

> The laverock and the lintie,
>   The robin and the wren;
> If ye harry their nests
>   Ye'll never thrive again.

Let me digress here for a moment. "Laverock" is scottish for lark, meaning the skylark. De Gubernatis,[54] who discourses learnedly on the mythical connotations of the name in India and ancient Greece, finds that the significance of this bird in popular tales is due to its crest, which he shows to be an indication that it was among the birds of the sun. "The crested lark," he says, "is the same as the crested sun, the sun with its rays," and he continues: "In the legend of St. Christopher I see an equivoque between the word *Christos* and the word *cresta,* crest, and either way I see the sun personified."

Whatever these speculations may be worth the old stories attribute to the lark that funereal charity which belongs to several birds, among them the European robin; and this brings us back to the main track and to the pretty story of the Babes in the Woods. Away back in bad old times a Norfolk gentleman left legacies to two infant children, which were to pass to their uncle if the babies died. After a year this uncle hired ruffians to take the children into a forest and kill them, but instead the men left them there to starve. For a time they ate blackberries, but soon became exhausted, lay down, and went to sleep, and expired.

> Their little corpse the robin-redbreast found,
> And strew'd with pious bill the leaves around.[8]

More modern poets have made many allusions to this touching tale, which Shakespeare knew, for in *Cymbeline* he makes Arviragus say over Imogen—

> Thou shalt not lack
> The flowers that's like thy face, pale primrose; nor
> The azured harebell. . . . The ruddock would
> With charitable bill bring thee all these.

And in William Collins's *Dirge to Cymbeline* are the lines:

> The redbreast oft at evening hours
> Shall kindly lend his little aid,
> With heavy moss, and gathered flowers,
> To deck the ground where thou art laid.

The conceit is far more ancient than Shakespeare or Gay or even than Robert Yarrington—who, in 1601, wrote a ballad on it concluding,

> No buriall this pretty pair of any man receives
> Till Robin Redbreast piously did cover them with leaves—

for Horace relates in one of his poems how he as a child wandering one day on Mount Vultur fell wearily asleep, and was covered by protecting doves with laurel and myrtle leaves.

The robin is always remembered at Christmas in the rural villages and farms of northern Europe, for it is not migratory. In South Germany the custom is to put grain on a roof for the redbreasts, who come trustfully about houses at that season, and find welcome shelter in barns and straw-stacks: and in Sweden and elsewhere an unthreshed sheaf of wheat is set up on a pole for their winter fare.

It will have been noticed that in the ballads quoted, the wren is associated with the robin in a protective way. A whole book might be written about this least of birds, which, although the least, is called "king" in every European language. We are told that a wren was in the stable at Bethlehem when Christ was born; and an Irish proverb runs: "The robin and the wren are God's two holy men." How surprising, then, to read of a custom called Hunting (or in some places Burying) the Wren, which once prevailed in southern France, in Keltic parts of England, in Wales, and also in Ireland, where it persisted until abolished by the British Government about the middle of the 19th century. Accounts of the practices, songs, etc., connected with it may be found in antiquarian histories, for example the following from Miles's book of Christmas customs:

In the Isle of Man very early on Christmas morning, when the church-bells had rung out midnight, servants went out to hunt the wren. They killed the bird, fastened it to the top of a long pole; and carried it in procession to every house, chanting these words:

> We hunted the wren for Robin the Bobbin,
>   We hunted the wren for Jack of the Can,
> We hunted the wren for Robin the Bobbin,
>   We hunted the wren for everyone.

At each house they sought to collect money. At last, when all had been visited, they laid the wren on a bier, carried it to the church-yard, and buried it with the utmost solemnity, singing Manx dirges.

It is evident that this is a very ancient practice, and embodies in its utterly degenerate state a religious idea or symbolism, the meaning of which has been forgotten. Why, for example, should the feathers of the murdered Manx wrens be preserved, one by one, among the coast families, as a talisman preserving the possessor from shipwreck, unless some religious sanction was involved, and this may be connected with St. Stephen, the first Christian martyr, who was stoned to death; for this savage custom belonged to St. Stephen's Day, December 26, as well as to Christmas, or locally in place of Christmas. But why the wren, rather than some other bird? The matter is

interesting enough to justify quoting the broad account
of the matter furnished by Swann:[47]

> An old Irish custom on St. Stephen's Day, and one that
> has not quite died out, was the "hunting of the wren" by boys.
> When captured it was tied, alive but maimed, to a pole (or,
> according to Vallancey—De Reb. Hib., IV, 13—tied by the
> leg in the center of two hoops placed at right angles with one
> another) and paraded around the neighborhood, a few doggerel
> verses being repeated at each house, while a donation was re-
> quested, one version being;
>
> > The wran, the wran, the king of all birds,
> > St. Stephen's Day was caught in the furze,
> > Come, give us a bumper, or give us a cake,
> > Or give us a copper, for Charity's sake.
>
> Yarrell records a similar practice in Kerry, where the peasantry
> on Christmas Day used to hunt the bird with two sticks, "one to
> beat the bushes the other to fling at the bird."   Bullock also
> mentions it as prevalent in the Isle of Man, both on Christmas
> Eve and St. Stephen's Day, and tells us it was founded on a
> tradition of a beautiful fairy who lured the male inhabitants
> to a watery grave in the sea, and who to escape subsequent de-
> struction took the form of a wren, which form she was sup-
> posed to be doomed by a spell to reassume each succeeding New
> Year's Day, ultimately perishing by human hands. . . . To my
> own knowledge this custom of a "wren hunt" existed in Not-
> tinghamshire also within recent times, the bird being hunted
> along the hedgerows by boys armed with stones, but I do not
> recollect that anything was done with the bird when killed or
> maimed. . . .
>
> In connection with this belief [alluded to above] in the king-
> ship over other birds, a Twelfth Day custom of parading a
> caged wren in Pembrokeshire, with the lines recited, is described
> in Swainson's Folklore of British Birds, O'Curry has recorded
> that the wren, like the raven, was kept domesticated on account
> of the auguries derived from it, which were employed by the
> Druids. An Irish proverb asserts that "The fox is the cunning-
> est beast in the world barring the wren." According to Dalyell
> the wren is considered an unlucky token in Scotland, but the
> robin a lucky one.

Explanations of this revolting yet long persistent custom have been many and various. A totemic sort of theory is that the bird "was once regarded as sacred, and the Christmas hunting is the survival of an annual custom of slaying the divine animal, such as is found among primitive peoples. The carrying of its body from door to door is apparently intended to convey to each house a portion of its virtues." I know of no facts in history to support this theory as applied to the Keltic race. One authority tells us that the "crime" for which the bird must be punished so ferociously is that it has "a drop o' the de'il's blood in its veins," but so has the magpie, which is not persecuted.

Lady Wilde [60] assures us that "the wren is mortally hated by the Irish for on one occasion, when the Irish troops were approaching to attack a portion of Thomas Cromwell's army the wrens came and perched on the Irish drums, and by their tapping and noise aroused the English soldiers, who fell on the Irish troops and killed them all." For this tragic incident we are given no time or place; and it happens that the same report was made respecting a battle between Irish and Danish invaders some 800 years before Cromwell's campaigns in the Emerald Isle or anywhere else.

The real clue to the puzzle is contained in the fact that in their barbarous hunt for wrens the men and boys kept yelling words that in Cormac's *Glossary* (10th century) are explained as "draoi-en," Druid-bird. We know that the Druid priests were accustomed to draw auguries from the chirpings of the wren—a divination to which the early Christian missionaries objected strenuously. It is probable that they condemned the little songster as a symbol of heathen rites, and encouraged their converts to

kill it at the time of the annual Christian feast as a sign
of abnegation of Druidical connections. The stoning of
the birds on St. Stephen's Day might be regarded as a
vengeful reminder of the manner of that martyr's
murder by a mob.

One more bird-story is connected with Christianity in
general—that alluded to in *Hamlet,* where Ophelia says:
"Well, God 'ield you! They say the owl was a baker's
daughter!" This enigmatical remark probably had reference to the story formerly, and perhaps still, common among the peasantry in the English Midlands, of a
baker's daughter that was transformed into an owl by
Jesus as a punishment for reducing to a very small size
the large piece of dough which her mother had agreed
to bake for him. The dough, however, swelled in the
oven to enormous proportions, to the girl's great astonishment, and she gasped out "Heu, heu, heu!" This owl-
like noise suggested her transformation into that bird.
The story is told to children as a warning lesson against
illiberal treatment of the poor. It is evidently alluded to,
also, in Beaumont and Fletcher's play *The Nice Valour,*
where the Passionate Lord says, after speaking of a nest
of owls, "Happy is he whose window opens to a brown
baker's chimney! he shall be sure there to hear the bird
sometimes after twilight." In northern Germany they
say a baker's man was the offender; and that he was
changed by Jesus into a cuckoo, the white spots in whose
wings show where the flour was sprinkled on the man's
dun coat. The Norse people apply the same moral by
means of their common woodpecker, whose pattern of
dress is indicated in the legend known to Norse children
as the Gertrud story, which is prettily related by Miss
Walker. [89] Brewer's *Handbook* notes that a maid-ser-

vant of the Virgin Mary, who had purloined one of her
mistress's dresses, was converted into a lapwing and condemned forever to cry "Tyvit, tyvit!" (I stole it). The
source of the anecdote is not given, nor the language of
the one who interprets it, but it reminds one of Tennyson's.

> With a lengthened loud halloo,
> Tuwhoo, tuwhit, tuwhit, tuwhoo-o-o.

The Greeks, according to Andrew Lang, had a similar
legend of feminine impiety, by which they mystically explained the origin of owls and bats.

The prevalence of a belief in such transformations as
these by Jesus is very widespread; the traditions vary
somewhat, as we have seen, in different countries, but it is
evident that the root is in the primitive notion that such
miracles were not only possible, but natural. Rather
more remote and obscure is the connection of birds with
certain other religious feasts, such as the substitution of
turkey for boar's-head as the central dish for the Christmas dinner among the English Dissenters, attributed to
the fact that turkeys became common about the time of
the Reformation, and acquired a meritorious character
on that account among those who wanted to continue the
Christmas feast without the taint of a dish partaking of
the customs of the hated Papists. Is our New England
custom of a turkey dinner on Thanksgiving Day traceable to this, remembering that the Puritans paid little or
no heed to Christmas?

For centuries, and until comparatively recent times,
among the sports and jollifications recalling the Roman
carnival (at the same date) that marked Shrove Tuesday,
the last day before Lent, both in Britain and in France,

along with the eating of unlimited pancakes, cock-fighting and "throwing at cocks" had the most prominent place. The last-mentioned sport consisted in fastening live cocks in a certain position, and letting men compete in throwing clubs at them, the man who killed the bird winning it. This atrocious form of amusement did not shock the populace of a time when bear-baiting, bull-baiting, and the pitting of dogs against each other or against badgers and rats were popular; yet a few protested, and even in the 17th century antiquaries were searching for the origin of the custom. Hearne asserted that it was in memory of English victories over the French (symbolized by the Gallic *coq*) in the time of Henry V; but the sport was customary in France itself long before that time. A writer quoted by Smith [61] records that "the common account of it is that the crowing of a cock prevented our Saxon ancestors from massacring their conquerors, the Danes, on the morning of a Shrove Tuesday while asleep in their beds," which recalls one of the explanations of the Irish wren-hunting. My own opinion is that the custom had no particular significance, but was just a sportive way of getting without much cost the material for a good dinner, as were the "turkey shoots" of our western frontier; and that Erasmus was fairly right when he remarked that "the English eat a certain cake on Shrove Tuesday, on which they immediately run mad and kill the poor cocks."

Lent closes with the joyful celebration of Easter, an occasion in which the eggs of birds, at least, have a persistent and prominent part, and doves find a place in several Old World ceremonies of the Church.

In the matter of the almost universal and everywhere popular custom of playing with colored eggs at Easter,

I can do no better than quote *The Catholic Encyclopedia,* article "Easter":

Because the use of eggs was forbidden during Lent they were brought to the table on Easter Day, colored red to symbolize the Easter joy. This custom is found not only in the Latin but also in the Oriental Churches. The symbolic meaning of a new creation of mankind by Jesus risen from the dead was probably an invention of later times. The custom may have its origin in Paganism, for a great many pagan customs, celebrating the return of spring, gravitated to Easter. The egg is the emblem of the germinating life of early spring. Easter eggs, the children are told, come from Rome with the bells which on Thursday go to Rome and return Saturday morning. The sponsors in some countries give Easter eggs to their god-children. Colored eggs are used by children at Easter in a sort of game which consists in testing the strength of the shells. Both colored and uncolored eggs are used in some parts of the United States in this game, known as "egg-picking." Another practice is the "egg-rolling" by children on Easter Monday on the lawn of the White House in Washington.

A quaint feature in this pagan survival in a Christian celebration of a momentous incident and idea is the connection with it of the rabbit. Wherever colored Easter eggs are displayed, images of a rabbit are likely to accompany them. Children are told that the Easter Rabbit lays the eggs, for which reason they are, in some countries, hidden in a nest in the garden. The strangeness of the association disappears when we remember that the date of the feast is determined by the time when the moon first becomes full after the spring equinox, and that the rabbit, which has from time immemorial been a symbol of fertility, is representative of the moon-goddess, Luna, which was worshipped annually at a date coinciding with the Easter festival. Thus, like many other pagan rites and symbols significant of reviving nature, it became confused with the Christian celebration of the Resurrection.

At the feast of the Pentecost, on Whitsunday, commemmorating the descent of the Holy Ghost upon the Apostles, doves were formerly always employed in Europe in staging the solemnities.

On Whitsuntide, white pigeons tame in strings from heaven fly,
And one that framed is of wood still hangeth in the skie,

as we are told by Neogeorgus (1511-63), speaking of the custom in Germany; and elsewhere we learn that in Spain pigeons with cakes tied to their legs were let loose in churches, where representations of the Holy Ghost were a part of the celebration. This last fact accounts for the use of the dove—an emblem of the third element of the God head, as we shall see.

To a similar old custom, if Marion Crawford, the learned author of *Salve Venetia*, is not mistaken, we owe the picturesque fact that pigeons are a feature of the plaza of St. Mark in Venice—one of the "sights" of that wonderful city:

The Venetians always loved processions, and it is to one of these pageants that the pigeons of St. Mark's owe their immunity. As early as the end of the fourteenth century it was the custom to make a great procession on Palm Sunday, in the neighborhood of St. Mark's. A canon of the Cathedral deposited great baskets on the high altar containing the artificial palms prepared for the Doge, the chief magistrates, and the most important members of the clergy. . . . According to the appointed service the procession began immediately after the distribution of the palms; and while the choir chanted the words *"Gloria, laus et honor"* of the sacred hymn, a great number of pigeons were sent flying from different parts of the façade down into the square, having little screws of paper fastened to their claws to prevent them from flying too high. The people instantly began to catch the birds, and a great many were actually taken; but now and then one, stronger than the rest, succeeded in gaining the higher parts of the surrounding buildings, enthusiastically cheered by the crowd.

Those who had once succeeded in making their escape were regarded as sacred forever with all their descendants. The state provided them with food from its granaries, and before long, lest by mistake any free pigeons should be caught on the next Palm Sunday the Signory next decreed that other birds must be used on the occasion.

F. Hopkinson Smith, in his *Gondola Days,* gives a more secular account of the origin of the regard felt by the Venetians for these "pets of the State," whose ancestor, the genial artist writes, brought the good news to Venice of the capture (in 1205) of Candia by Admiral Enrico Dandolo.

CHAPTER VII

BIRDS AS SYMBOLS AND BADGES

CERTAIN kinds of birds have become symbols of popular ideas, or even significant badges of persons and events, and are thus more or less conventionalized accessories in art, by reason of their appearance (form, color), or their habits, or their connection with some historic incident or fabulous tale. In many cases this symbolism is of very ancient origin, as is most particularly true of the eagle and the dove. The eagle is accounted for elsewhere in its various aspects and relations: but the dove, by which is meant the prehistorically domesticated blue rock-pigeon, almost deserves a chapter to itself.

To trace the career of the dove in religion, customs, and art is, indeed, one of the most engaging of my tasks, and the quest discloses a curiously double and diverse symbolism running almost simultaneously from the beginning of history to the present, for this bird serves as an emblem of purity and conjugal affection in one association, and in another suggests the familiar epithet "soiled."

The story of this bird goes back to the misty dawn of civilization and religion in Mesopotamia, the Garden-of-Eden land, where arose the dual "nature-worship" of the combining elements heaven and earth, male and female. The fecund soil, yielding its fruits to the fertilizing sunshine and rain, sent by the sky-god, became personified as Ishtar (Ashtaroth), and to her was assigned the amorous and prolific dove as a type of the family concord and productiveness she represented; and white doves were sold to worshippers at Babylon to be offered as sacrifices in her temple. Her worship was spread to Asia Minor and the shore of the Ægean by Babylonian and Assyrian conquests, and she became known to the Phrygians as Cybele, to the Syrians as Darketo, and to the Phoenicians as Atagartis, whom the Ionian Greeks called Astarte.

In these transformations the primitive Ishtar gradually fell from her original state as a type of motherhood to the baser one of physical love-indulgence, and among her votaries were troops of maidens who publicly offered their virginity at her shrine, as a form of sacrifice and service.

Some of the Syrians are said to have thought of their goddess Darketo as "Semiramis," but this was by confusion with her fabled daughter. Whether or not a real woman and queen of that name ever existed, I leave to the historians, but a mythical Semiramis belongs to my story, and her history was first written by Ctesias, an Asiatic-Greek historian of the fourth century B.C. Ctesias says that near Askalon was a large lake beside which Darketo (otherwise Atagartis) had a habitation; she is represented with the face of a woman and the body of a fish—perhaps the most antique conception of a mermaid. She fell in love with a fair youth and a girl-baby resulted. Then, in shame, Darketo destroyed her lover, exposed the child in a rocky desert, and flung herself into the lake. The babe, nurtured by doves on milk and cheese, was discovered and reared by a herdsman, who called the child Semiramis—a Syrian word for "doves." At the close of her life this mythical Semiramis changed herself into a dove and flew away with certain other birds. Hence, in Ctesias's time, divine honors were paid in the East to doves; and a dove is the badge of Semiramis in Syrian monumental art. Diodorus Siculus repeats this account with additional details.

The sceptre in the hand of the revered image of Atagartis in her great temple at Hierapolis bore the golden figure of a dove on its summit; and in Phoenicia, Cyprus, Sardinia, and wherever the Phocians and other Levantine traders of that day traded and colonized, have been found small terra-cotta figures of this goddess, or of one of her priestesses, always with a dove.

To the devotees of this cult, which was confined to the coastal region, and in which the Hebrews and other Semites of the interior desert-plains took no part, a dove was so sacred that if a person even accidentally touched one he was "unclean" throughout the day. Hence the birds thronged in the villages and houses and swarmed about the temple yards, where they were fed by visitors, as still is the custom in the Mohammedan mosques that have taken their place. This was noted especially at Hierapolis, where, according to Lucian, one of the venerated images had a pigeon's head.

This religious doctrine, and more particularly the Phrygian cult of Cybele, was undoubtedly carried to the Ægean islands and to Greece, while civilization was still in its infancy there, for the "sea-born" Aphrodite—an epithet indicative of her arrival from across the waters—is only Astarte transformed in Greek thought, which seems to explain the classic story that Aphrodite was born from an egg, with a dove brooding upon it, rolled ashore by a fish.

The focus of religious emotion in those early centuries of Greece, at least in Attica, was probably in the most

ancient of oracles, that at Dodona. Tradition ascribed its
origin to a dove that spoke with a human voice; and
among those who served the shrine were three priestesses
popularly called "Doves," whose duty it was to announce
oracles requested as if real birds uttered them from the
foliage of the surrounding oaks—divine trees. Connected with the cult of Zeus at Dodona was that of
Aphrodite, then regarded as the goddess of exalted love,
not of the sensual passion by which in later times her cult
in Rome, as Venus, became degraded. It was natural,
as we have seen, that the dove should be associated with
this pristine Aphrodite, and equally suitable that it should
be adopted subsequently as the attendant of lascive
Venus, for as De Kay [18] observes, doves are forever making love and caressing each other. "Chaucer speaks of
'the wedded turtil with her herte trewe'. . . . So the
bird is by its nature and habits fitted to be the attendant
and symbol of the goddess of love—the bird that draws
her flower-studded chariot through the air." A Persian
poet asks:

> Knowest thou why round his neck the dove
>   A collar wears?—it is to tell
> He is the faithful slave of love,
>   And serves all those who serve him well.[88]

An interesting memorandum here is the observation by
A. B. Cook,[87] the erudite author of *Zeus,* that the oracle
in the oasis Ammon (Siwah), which Alexander the
Great took such prodigious trouble to visit and consult,
was, like that at Dodona, founded by a dove. "Moreover," Mr. Cook remarks, "Semiramis is said to have
learned her destiny from Ammon, and to have fulfilled
it by becoming a dove. . . . In short, it appears that the

whole apparatus of the oracle at Dodona . . . was to be matched in the oasis of Ammon. Strabo adds that both oracles gave their responses in the selfsame manner, not by words but by certain tokens, such as the flight of doves."

The conception of Aphrodite also included that of spring, ushered in by the early return of this migrant from its winter resort in Africa and the time when it cooed for a mate—the season when "a livelier iris changes on the burnished dove"; while the revival of nature in spring has always to imaginative souls typified the Resurrection as taught in Christian doctrine and exemplified in some of the customs of Easter, which, of course, is only an adaptation of the far more ancient festival of rejoicing at the return of the sun—the rebirth of the year.

Another line of thought apparently of Oriental origin, but prevalent in northern Europe, connected this dove with the Fates and with death, especially death by violence—a phase that is traced in wearisome detail back to the *Rigvedas* and other misty sources by the myth-readers, and which probably comes from its plaintive "cooing." Sometimes, however, the fateful dove brings good tidings and succor to the distressed, as in the story of Queen Radegund, who in the form of a dove once delivered sailors from shipwreck.

This is an appropriate place, perhaps, to repeat the legend related by the Rhodian Apollonius in his poem *Argonautica,* concerning the Symplegades—the two islands that stand on opposite sides of the Bosphorus "mouth." It appears that these islands were wont in days ancient even to Apollonius to swing together and crush any living thing that attempted to pass between them and enter the Black Sea. Phineas, who lived on the shore near by told Jason, who had arrived there on his journey in search of the Golden Fleece, and who wanted to go on into the Euxine, how to escape the fatal grasp of the island-gates. He was to sail or row the *Argo* as near as he dared to the entrance, then let loose a dove. The bird would fly onward, the islands would rush together to crush it; and the instant they had swung back Jason must drive his ship on between them before they could close again. This plan, so clever except for the poor bird, succeeded, and broke the magic spell. Living heroes had passed safely between them, and ever since then the malicious Symplegades have remained stable. This story has been scientifically analyzed by the mythologists in various ways, but none has deigned to consider why a dove was chosen, rather than some other bird, as the martyr of the occasion. I am inclined to think it was because among sailors of those days the dove was believed to help them; and that, in turn, was owing to its association with the "foam-born" Aphrodite, who was worshipped by mariners, especially about Cyprus, as goddess of the sea.

I have dwelt somewhat at length on these antique fables, not only to give a glimpse of the nativity of certain far more modern, or even existing, ideas and customs connected with the dove, but more especially to display the background of tradition and feeling that affected the minds of people toward this familiar bird at the time when Christianity began to manifest itself in Italy, and began to replace by a Christian symbolism the previous figurative significance of the dove. The highest place given it in early Christian thought and art was as a representative of the third member of the godhead— the Holy Ghost, and it still holds this significance, as every one may realize who recalls the hymn beginning "Come Holy Spirit, heavenly Dove," which will be sung in perhaps hundreds of churches next Sunday. An old and natural inference followed, that the devil cannot ever take (by magic) the form of this celestial messenger.

According to an apocryphal gospel the Holy Ghost in the semblance of a dove, designated Joseph as the spouse of the Virgin Mary by alighting on his head; and in the same manner, according to Eusebius, Fabian was indicated as divinely appointed to be Pope in the third century. It is said also that at the Council of Nice (A. D. 325) the creed formulated there was signed by the Holy Spirit, appearing as a dove—a legend that magnifies the tremendous importance of that document.

Again, there is the story of the miraculous dove at the consecration of Clovis on Christmas Day, 496, at Rheims. When Clovis and St. Remi, the bishop, reached the baptistery the priest bearing the holy chrism was prevented by the density of the crowd from reaching the font. Then a dove, whiter than snow, brought a vial (ampoule) filled with chrism sent from heaven; and the bishop took it, and with this miraculous chrism perfumed the baptismal water for the Frankish chief by whose victories over Germanic barbarians France was founded.

The lives of medieval saints and martyrs—or at any rate, the records of them—abound in such incidents of supernatural recognition. Several devoted women on taking the vow of virginity received their veils from doves hatched in no earthly nest; bishops were more than once given approval of public acts, especially when unpopular, by similar manifestations of divine approbation, doves alighting on their heads. "A dove is the special emblem of Gregory the Great (A. D. 590-604), and its

figure rests on his right shoulder in the magnificent statue
of this pope in Rome."

This is in allusion, according to *The Catholic Encyclopedia,* "to the well-known story recorded by Peter the
Deacon (*Vita,* xxviii), who tells us that when the pope
was dictating his homilies in Ezechiel a veil was drawn
between his secretary and himself. As, however, the
pope remained silent for long periods of time, the servant
made a hole in the curtain and, looking through, beheld
a dove seated on Gregory's head with its beak between
his lips. When the dove withdrew its beak the holy
pontiff spoke and the secretary took down his words; but
when he became silent the servant again applied his eyes
to the hole and saw that the dove had again placed its
beak between his lips." Much the same incident belongs
to the biography of another early pope; and apropos to
the significance of this bird in the Romanist method of
demonstrating that faith to the populace, Mackenzie E.
Walcott contributed the following bit of history to *Notes
and Queries* in 1873:

The dove was regarded as the symbol of the holy spirit
which came in the eventide of days, bringing safety and peace
to the ark of Christ and a world rescued from wreck, and to
whom Christians should be conformed in innocency. A dove
was suspended over the altar, as Amphilochius says of S. Basil
that he broke the Holy Bread and placed one third part in the
pendant golden dove over the altar. The Council of Constantinople charged a heretic with robbing the gold and silver doves
that hung above the fonts and altars. The dove was also the
symbol of our Blessed Lord, as we learn from Prudentius and
an expression of Tertullian, "the Dove's house," applied to a
church, probably in allusion to Coloss. i, 20.

The dove for reservation [that is, withholding a part of the
eucharist] whether for communion of infants in the baptistery,
or of sick under a ciborium, was suspended by a chain. One is
preserved in the church of S. Nazarius at Milan, and a solitary

mention of another is contained in an inventory of Salisbury. In Italy at an early date, the dove was set upon a tower for reservation. . . . We also find in early works of devotional art the dove represented as flooding a cross with streams of living water. There is a famous example in the Lateran, symbolical of Holy Baptism. A holy lamb and dove are placed on the canopy of the baptistery at Saragossa.

It seems unlikely that Mohammed could have heard of these pontifical sources or methods of divine inspiration, yet, according to Brewer,[34] Prideaux, in his *Life of Mahamet,* relates that he taught a dove to pick seed placed in his ear as it perched on his shoulder; but the wily prophet "gave it out it was the Holy Ghost, in the form of a dove, come to impart to him the counsels of God." This accounts probably (for Shakespeare may well have heard the tradition) for the doubting query in *Henry V:* "Was Mohammed inspired with a dove?"

Whether this legend is credible or not, it is certain that Islam has preserved the ancient Oriental reverence for this bird, which now flocks in great numbers around all the mosques; and the Moslems have a half-super-stitious feeling that any bird that seeks its rest and makes its nest about temples and holy buildings must not be disturbed—a kindly regard in which swallows share, at least in the Near East, where the Mohammedans say that the swallow must be a very holy bird, because it makes an annual pilgrimage to Mecca.

John Keane,[14] an Englishman who spent a long time in Arabia about forty years ago, records that at Mecca vast flocks of pigeons were to be seen in the public space surrounding the kaaba. By repeated observations he esti-mated that between 5000 and 6000 pigeons assembled there daily, all so tame that they would alight on men's heads and shoulders. They are still held as almost sacred, are never killed, and nest in nearly every building in niches left for that purpose in the walls of the rooms. Pilgrims purchase baskets of grain to give to the pigeons as a pious act, and each benefactor "becomes the vortex of a revolving storm of pigeons." In some remote places, indeed, these temple-pets become themselves almost objects of worship. For example, on the direct road between Yarkand and Khotan, Chinese Turkestan, stands the locally celebrated pigeon-shrine (Kaptar Mazzar), where all good Moslems must dismount and reverently approach the sacred spot. "Legend has it that Imam Shakir Padshah, trying to convert the Buddhist inhabitants of the country to Islam by the drastic agency of the sword, fell here in battle against the army of Khotan, and was buried in the little cemetery. It is affirmed that two doves flew forth from the heart of the dead saint, and became the ancestors of the swarms of pigeons we saw . . . sated with the offerings of the Faithful, and extremely fat. . . . We were told that if a hawk were to venture to attack them it would fall down dead."

A pretty story is related by E. Dinet, a French artist, in his book of sketches in Algeria. "Doves, which the Arabs name imams, because," he was told, "like the imam in the mosques, they call the faithful to prayer, and because, like him, they do not cease to prostrate themselves by inclining their necks in devotions to the Creator."

Newspapers of the year 1921 contained an account of how two European boys ignorantly provoked a riot in Bombay by killing a couple of pigeons in the street. The Mohammedans were horrified and the police had difficulty in supressing an extensive disturbance; the stock exchange and other general markets were closed, and a

wide-spread strike of workmen in India was threatened, as
an evidence of the deep feeling aroused by the boys'
sacrilegious act. It was evidence also of the panic-force
of superstition under an appropriate stimulus, and a good
illustration of Professor George Santayana's definition
of superstition as "reverence for what hurts." In the
same year it was reported by telegraph from Brownsville,
Texas, that a snow-white pigeon flew into Sacred Heart
Church there on the morning of November 11, during a
service celebrating Armistice Day, and perched over a
memorial window, where it remained throughout the
service. Had it been a sparrow or woodpecker no one
would have thought of recording the incident.

Men in the Middle Ages had perfect faith in prodigies
such as those connected with the holy ampoule of St.
Remi and the subsequent miracles in which it was so
efficacious; and everyone understood their meaning. This
continued as long as the Church held sway over hearts
and minds of the populace. Nobody, probably, had the
disposition, not to say the hardihood, to deny the story—
you may read it in Froissart—that at the battle of Roose-
beek (or Rosebeque), which put an end to the power of
Philip van Artevelde in 1382, a white dove was seen to
circle about and alight on the French oriflame, which
then swept on to victory.

Readers of Malory's *Morte D'Arthur* will recall that
as on its appearance the Holy Grail passes before Lance-
lot's eyes in the castle of Pelleas, a dove, entering at the
window and carrying a small golden censer in its beak,
impressed the awe-struck knights of the Table Round as
a lovely token of the purity and worship to which the
castle was devoted. Nothing could be more natural in
medieval romance than this incident—a miracle com-

memorated in the opera *Parsifal*. The Venetians still
assert that the pigeons so familiar and petted in the piazza
of St. Mark fly three times daily around the city in honor
of the Trinity.

A later example: in the first voyage of Hernando
Cortez to America water and food were almost exhausted,
and everybody in the vessel was discouraged and
mutinous, when "came a Dove flying to the Shippe, being
Good Friday at Sunsett; and sat him on the Shippe-top;
whereat they were all comforted, and tooke it for a
miracle and good token . . . and all gave heartie thanks
to God, directing their course the way the Dove flew."
Any sort of bird would have been welcome as an indication of nearness of land, but a *dove* meant to them a
heavenly pilot. No wonder that they were comforted!
And when they had landed they found in abundance a
flower (the orchid *Peristeria elata*) which they at once
named La Flor del Espiritu Santu—Flower of the Holy
Ghost. Why? Because in its center the consolidated
pistil and stamens form an unmistakable image of a dove.

The immediate source of this symbolism is evidently
the account in the gospels of the divine sanction witnessed
at the baptism of Jesus. Matthew (iii, 16) records: "Lo,
the heavens were opened unto him, and he saw the Spirit
of God descending like a dove, and lighting upon him";
and St. Luke strengthens the realism by writing that
"the Holy Ghost descended in a bodily shape like a dove."
Hence this bird is constantly associated with Christ and
with the Cross by artists and decorative designers; and
it is no wonder that in so strictly Catholic countries as
Italy it is considered sacrilegious by many of the people
to eat the flesh of pigeons.

"In the fifth century," as Mrs. Jenner tells us in her

book on Christian symbolism,[63] the dove is shown descending on the Blessed Virgin at the Annunciation. After this date the Holy Dove is commonly shown in depicting both these subjects, as well as the sacrament of baptism. It appears frequently also over the pictures of the Virgin and Child, and in pictures of the Creation, where "the spirit of God moved on the face of the waters. . . . The Holy Spirit as a dove bestowing the Gift of Tongues is shown with flames oroceeding from Him."

The prophet Elisha is represented in a window of Lincoln College, England, with a two-headed dove on his shoulder—evidently an allusion to his petition to Elijah (*II Kings,* ii, 9): "I pray thee, let a double portion of thy spirit be upon me."

But this venerated bird has many other meanings in Christian art and parable, sometimes so comprehensive as to include the Church, or Pope, or Christians generally in the sense that they are distinguished from Pagans by their gentleness and innocence.

Reference has been made to the funereal quality of this bird, which appears on medieval funerary monuments as testimony of death in Christian faith. In the miracle-play depicting the career and martyrdom of St. Eulalia of Barcelona, which is still enacted annually in the Catalan village-churches of the eastern Pyrenees, it is represented that the tortured soul of the Christian maiden escapes to heaven in the form of a dove. Even to-day one sees these birds, or a pair of them, carved on tombstones, or their stuffed skins employed as a part of funeral wreaths and accessories, and certain superstitions have grown out of this practice, as is related elsewhere.

The white domestic dove has always been a figure of

purity by reason, no doubt, of its whiteness, as of un-
stained snow or light—the same feeling that prescribes
white raiment in such church services as the confirmation
of girls, and white veils and flowers for brides. This,
probably, was the reason, too, why white doves, and even
geese, were acceptable for sacrifice in the Jewish temple
of old from those who could not afford to give a lamb.
Mary, mother of Jesus, offered doves at her sacrificial
purification; and that these birds were commonly used for
that purpose is evident from the fact that a great trade in
them had grown up in and around the temple in
Jerusalem, profaning it, so that later Jesus drove away
from its hallowed precincts "them that sold doves." A
tradition says that Moses, a good economist, decreed as a
proper sacrifice-offering either a turtle-dove or two young
pigeons, because doves were good to eat at any time,
whereas pigeons (the larger and wilder stock) were tough
and unpalatable except as squabs; and it is to be remembered that the edible flesh of sacrificed animals was
afterward eaten, and for that end was divided equally between the offerer and the priests.

A more widespread, popular and persistent notion
makes the dove the symbol of peace, usually depicted with
a spray of olive in its beak. How the olive came to have
this character has been thoroughly discussed by the Rev.
H. Friend.[11] It appears to be largely an accidental
acquisition, even if one believes that the idea is derived
from the olive-leaf brought back by the dove that Noah
sent forth from the ark. In old times a tree-branch of
any sort served as does a modern flag of truce between
warring factions; or was held aloft as a sign of friendly
intentions when strangers approached others without

hostile purpose. The tradition of the Deluge suggested, and usage has strengthened, the supposition that the olive was the proper sort of branch to show (without danger of misunderstanding), as was the practice of Roman heralds, and the fact that this bird was associated with the olive in Biblical legend has made the dove the "bird of peace." The olive-tree was given to Athens and the world by Pallas Athene, patron of peace and plenty.

As a matter of ornithology the choice of this bird as a representative of peace is an unfortunate one, for pigeons are unusually quarrelsome among themselves; it is noticeable, however, that in all these relations the symbolic dove is a white one—not the gray ring-dove. In Japan, on the contrary doves are considered messengers of war, which perhaps originated in the legend of an escape from his enemies by the mythical hero Yoritomo. He was hiding in a hollow tree, and when his pursuers saw two doves fly out of the hollow they concluded no one could be there and passed on. Yoritomo afterward became shogun, and he erected shrines to the god of war, whose birds are doves, become so, perhaps, by reason of their pugnacity.

Next to the dove (or perhaps the eagle) the peacock appears to have most importance among birds as a symbol. To us it stands as a vainglorious and foppish personality of very little use in a practical world; and India has a proverb that the crow that puts on peacock's feathers finds that they fall out and that he has left only the harsh voice. De Gubernatis [54] quotes another Hindoo saying, that this bird has angel's feathers, a devil's voice and a thief's walk. Other stories tell of the proud bird's chagrin when he looks down and perceives how black and

glossy are his feet—as old Robert Chester sang it in
Love's Martyr:

> The proud sun-loving peacocke with his feathers,
> Walkes all alone, thinking himself a king,
> And with his voyce prognosticates all weathers,
> Although God knows but badly doth he sing;
> But when he lookes downe to his base blacke feete,
> He droops, and is asham'd of things unmeete.

A still earlier poet had sung of this secret chagrin
attributed to the conceited fowl, and had accounted for
it by a popular Moslem tradition, illustrated to this day
by the fact that the Devil-worshipping sect of Yezd, in
northern Mesopotamia, reverence the peacock as the ac-
complice of Eblis, which is Satan; my reference is to the
Persian Azz' Eddin Elmocadessi,[88] who wrote—

> The peacock wedded to the world,
>   Of all her gorgeous plumage vain,
> With glowing banners wide unfurled,
>   Sweeps slowly by in proud disdain;
> But in her heart a torment lies,
> That dims the lustre of those eyes;
> She turns away her glance—but no,
> Her hideous feet appear below!
> And fatal echoes, deep and loud,
>   Her secret mind's dark caverns stir;
> She knows, though beautiful and proud,
>   That Paradise is not for her.
> For, when in Eden's blissful spot
>   Lost Eblis tempted man, she dared
> To join the treach'rous angel's plot
>   And thus his crime and sentence shared.
> Her frightful claws remind her well
> Of how she sinned and how she fell.

The native home of this resplendent pheasant is India
and Malaya, and the brilliance of its plumage (in the

male sex, to which all that follows refers), the radiating, rustling quills and prismatic eye-spots of the magnificent tail-coverts, together with other features of the bird's life, led to its association in Eastern mythology with the sun and sometimes with the rainbow. Taken westward by adventurous traders, the glittering dress of the cock entered into the popular conception of the phenix, and thus the peacock came to be accepted in pagan Greece and Italy as a substitute for that gorgeous fiction, as no real phenix was obtainable. Naturally the new bird was assigned, superseding her homely goose, to Hera (Juno) the consort of Zeus (Jupiter) whose cognizance was the eagle—the other component of the hybrid phenix; and, as Juno was queen of heaven, the bird was used by prechristian artists as the symbol of the apotheosis of an empress as was the eagle that of an emperor.

These ideas were of Eastern origin, and came with the bird when it was introduced into the western world from its home in southern Asia, where its harsh cry of warning to the jungle whenever it espied a tiger, leopard or big snake, was also a welcome signal to the people of the woodland villages to be on their guard. "For this reason, as well as its habit of foretelling rain by its dancing and cries of delight, it has from time immemorial been held in the East as a bird of magic, or the embodiment of some god of the forest whose beneficence is well worth supplication, and whose resentment might bring disaster. Hence it was ever protected, not by law, but from a feeling of veneration."

The words quoted are from one of a series of articles on Oriental Art by Mrs. Katherine M. Ball,[68] printed in *Japan* (July, 1922), from which the reader may gather

further facts as to the place the bird holds in the religious
and artistic thought of the Orient. In China, for example, in the time of the Tang dynasty (8th century,
A. D.), "many thousand districts," according to the
chronicles, "paid tribute in peacocks, because their
feathers were required by the state, not only as decorations for the imperial processions, but for the designation of official rank; for the peacock feather was bestowed upon officials, both military and civil, as a reward
for faithful service." Such feathers differed according
to the honor to be dispensed, hence there are the "flower"
feather, the "green" feather, and the "one-eyed," "two-
eyed" and "three-eyed," all of which were greatly
treasured and worn on special occasions. This use of the
feather is accounted for by Mrs. Ball in this way: "In
the Chin dynasty a defeated general took refuge in a
forest where there were many peacocks. When the pursuing forces arrived, and found the fowl so quiet and
undisturbed, they concluded that no one could possibly
have come that way, and forthwith abandoned the search.
The general—who later became known as the ancestor of
five kings—was thus able to escape, and so grateful was
he that later when he came into power he instituted the
custom of conferring a peacock feather as an honor for
the achievement of bravery in battle." This incident reminds us of the escape of Yoritomo of Japan, and of the
Tartar general who avoided capture under the protection
of a quiet owl, as related elsewhere.

The Japanese are fond of the peacock as a motive in
their exquisite art, and frequently combine it with the
peony, as do the Chinese, who consider that the only
flower worthy of such association. Another subject frequently seen illustrated is a representation of the Buddhist

healing deity Kujako Myowo, the Japanese analogue of the Hindoo deification of this fowl.

Whether the peacock was brought to the Mediterranean region from India or Persia or from Phoenicia is unknown. It is commonly said that Alexander the Great was its introducer; but wherever it went its symbolic significance accompanied it, otherwise the peoples of Greece and Italy would hardly have given it the name of their own goddess of light and day, or have held it to be a visible sign of the rainbow itself. In combination with the eagle it was originally an attribute of Pan, who later was obliged to yield it to Juno, the goddess of Heaven, thus making it the star-bird, the symbol of the starry firmament, on account of the "eyes" in its tail-feathers, which were regarded as the very stars themselves. Out of this arose many myths, chief among which is that of the hundred-eyed Argus—how Argus was set by Juno to watch Io, of whom she had been jealous, but was killed by Mercury in the interest of the queen's unrepentant husband; and how Juno makes the best of a bad situation:

> Thus Argus lies in pieces cold and pale;
> And all his hundred eyes with all their light
> Are closed at once in one perpetual night.
> These Juno takes, that they no more shall fail,
> And spreads them on her peacock's gaudy tail.[69]

But the Christians, in their revolt against everything Pagan, regarded this bird, which like so many other facts and fancies of the ancient régime they could not destroy, from a new and different angle. They observed that although it lost (by molting) its splendid raiment yet as often it was re-acquired—manifestly a similitude of the resurrection of the devoted soul into renewed glories

after death.   The fact was true, of course of all birds,
but it was most noticeable in this gaudy stranger from the
land of sunrise; and, in addition, a belief was borrowed
from the phenix that its flesh was incorruptible.   Thus
the peacock became in early Christian art a symbol of immortality.

In the general mental lethargy that marked the Middle
Ages this elevated idealism was degraded; yet that somewhat of the bird's traditional sacredness remained is
shown by the fact that among the customs of chivalry,
knights and squires took oath on the king's peacock,
which, stuffed and brought ceremoniously to the table,
was a feature in various solemnities.   Critics trace to
this the Shakespearian oath "By cock and pye!"—to my
mind a dubious gloss.   "It is said of Pythagoras," De
Gubernatis [54] notes, "that he believed himself to have once
been a peacock, that the peacock's soul entered into
Euphorbus, a Homeric Trojan hero, that of Euphorbus
into Homer, and that of Homer into him."   Those who
are familiar with classic literature may be able to continue the history of this literary metempsychosis down to
the present.   Hehn and Stallybrass elaborate their history
of the peacock in custom and myth in exhaustive detail in
their *Wanderings of Plants and Animals*.

A quaint relic of ancient ideas survives in the prevalent
notion that the beautiful tail-plumes of the peacock are
unlucky or worse, for it is widely feared that illness and
death speedily follow putting them into a house, especially
as affecting the health of youngsters.   It occurred to me
that this superstition, as foolish as it is baleful, was probably connected with the far-reaching dread of the Evil
Eye, having in mind the gleaming ocellæ that decorate
these   splendid   feathers,   but   Elworthy's   exhaustive

treatise [66] on that dreaded visitation (especially feared among Italians) alludes to the matter only casually, and expresses the opinion that the alleged ill-luck is a relic of the ancient cult of Juno—a lingering fear that in some way her anger may be excited by the plucking of the feathers of her favorite bird; while the idea that so long as these plumes are kept in the house no suitors will come for the daughters points to the old attribute of spite or jealousy in love or matrimonial matters with which Juno was always accredited in Pagan times.

It occurs to me, also, that the fact that the revered peacock throws away (moulds) its quills every year suggests to a superstitious imagination that they may be distasteful to the bird, and hence something to be avoided by careful devotees. Nevertheless, on Easter Day in Rome, when the pope is borne in magnificent state into St. Peter's, he waves over the heads of the reverent worshippers assembled there a fan (flabbellum) of ostrich feathers on which have been sewn the eye-spots from peacock plumes, the latter, we are told, signifying the all-seeing vigilance of the Church—against foolishness as well as downright evil, let us hope!

No bird is more often employed symbolically in Christian art than the pelican, which, like the peacock became a representative of salvation through the self-sacrifice of Christ. How this developed from the supposed habit of resuscitating her nestlings by feeding them blood from her bosom, after they had been murdered by the father, is explained in another chapter. It is said that the story originated in Egypt, with reference to a vulture. St. Jerome, however, first gave it a theological application, teaching that similarly those dead in sin were made alive again by the blood of the Christ. The form—still familiar in heraldry—is that of a bird sitting by its nest with its beak depressed and tearing at its breast, representing "the pelican in its piety," the last word here having its original meaning of parental care. It also became a pictured symbol of the Christ and of the Passion, "and more particularly of the Eucharist, wherein Christians are nourished by Christ himself." Thomas Aquinas (13th century) is the author of a well-known verse of this import:

> Pelican of Piety, Jesus, Lord and God,
> Cleanse thou me, unclean, in thy most precious blood,
> But a single drop of which doth save and free
> All the universe from its iniquity.

A similar stanza in John Skelton's *Armoury of Birds* reads:

> Then sayd the Pellycane,
> When my byrdts be slayne,
> With my bloude I them reuyue [revive].
> Scrypture doth record
> The same dyd our Lord,
> And rose from deth to lyue. [life]

The eagle is to be regarded rather as an emblem than as a symbol yet it has a significance of this sort, for by the early Christians it was considered a symbol of the Ascension. This may have been a pious inversion of the custom in Pagan Rome of setting free an eagle at the funeral pyre of an emperor, in the belief that this messenger of Jove would carry the dead monarch's soul straight up to Olympus.

The notion that in death the soul leaves the body in the form of a bird is old and very general. Medieval biographies of Christian saints and martyrs abound in instances, as, for example, the story of Saint Devoté,

found in a boat near Monaco at the moment of her expiring, with a dove issuing from her lips.[67]   The Paris
Figaro, in October, 1872, describing the ceremonies at
the death of a gipsy in that city, mentioned that a bird
was held close to the mouth of the dying girl, ready to receive her expired soul. This is not an illogical idea, if
the conception of a person's soul as a distinct entity is
conceded; for if it is to fly away to Paradise it must
have something in the nature of wings, and a bird, or the
semblance of a real bird, is inevitably suggested, the
wings of a bat being too repulsive—reserved, in fact, for
representations of Satan and his emissaries. Angels and
genii have always been provided by prophets, romancers,
and artists with swanlike wings, springing from behind
their shoulders, reckless of comparative anatomy—otherwise how could these "heavier-than-air" beings ac-
complish their travelling?

I have said that the theory that the disengaged soul de-
parts to heaven in the form of or by aid of a bird is
historically very old. Probably, indeed, it is of prehistoric antiquity, for various savage peoples have arrived
at the same doctrine, based on an obvious philosophy.
For example: Powers [19] tells us that the Keltas of
southern California believe that when one of the tribe dies
a little bird flies away with his soul. "If he was a bad
Indian a hawk will catch the bird and eat it up, body,
feathers and all; but if he was a good Indian the soul-
bird will reach the spirit-land."

In Christian iconography the eagle is the emblem of the
evangelist St. John, an assignment originating, it is said,
in Jerome's interpretation of the amazing visions of the
four "beasts" as recorded in *Ezekiel* i:5, and somewhat
less fantastically in *Revelations* iv:7. Wherever in

sculpture, painting, or stained glass St. John appears he
may be recognized by his eagle; and sometimes the bird
is rather more conspicuous than the saint, as when it is
bearing him aloft on its back, both gazing, open-eyed and
resolute, at the sun, as the eagle is fabled to be able to
do. This association also accounts for the practice of
carving the support of the reading-desk in both Catholic
and Anglican churches in the form of an eagle with
outstretched wings. At the beginning, we are told,
figures of all four evangelists upheld the lectern; but
one by one the others disappeared before the demands of
artistic grace until at last John, "the beloved disciple,"
alone remained, and presently he came to be represented
only by his emblem. "Medieval writers," remarks B. L.
Gales, in an article in *The National Review* (1808), "delight in all sorts of wild and wonderful tales about his,"
that is, the eagle's "renewing his youth by gazing at the
sun or plunging into a clear stream, and allegorize at
length on the Waters of Baptism and the true Sun—
Jesus Christ." This, of course, is simply a comparatively
modern illustration of the very ancient myth that when
the sun set in the western ocean, yet arose bright and hot
next morning, it had rejuvenated itself by its bath as it
passed from west to east underneath the world.

In the East, where the sport of falconry originated, and
where the Mongols trained and employed, and still do,
eagles as well as hawks, the falcon has acquired much
interesting symbolism, especially in Japan, as appears in
many exquisite drawings by early artists; and often these
can be fully understood and enjoyed by us of the West
only when the subtle meaning involved in the picture is
interpreted to us, or we learn the tradition to which it
refers. For example, in Hokusai's drawing *San Puku*

(The Three Lucky Things) the mountain symbolizes the beauty of nature, the falcon the delights of the chase, and the eggplant the wisdom of frugality and of the simplicity of life. This undaunted bird (*taka,* the heroic one) is to the Japanese the symbol of victory; and the Medal of Victory, which the government confers upon distinguished warriors has emblazoned upon it a golden falcon, in commemoration of the coming to Japan of its mythical ancestor, Jimmu Tenno; for it is related that as he set foot up on the Island's shore, a falcon flew toward him and lit on his bow, an incident which has ever been regarded as prophetic of the success of his undertaking.

Little can be added in this connection concerning the birds of prey. In ancient Egypt the vulture represented Nekht, the tutelary deity of the South, who appeared to men in that form; and the protection she accorded to the queens of Egypt was indicated by the vulture-head-dress worn by these ladies at least during the Empire. The kite, too, is connected with early Egyptian history, according to a tradition, preserved by Diodorus Siculus, that the book of religious laws and customs was originally brought to Thebes by a kite; wherefore the sacred scribes wore a red cap with a kite's feather in it.

The cock in Christian religious art is to be interpreted as an emblem of vigilance—also as an image of preachers, in which may be a touch of humor. "When introduced near the figure of St. Peter," says one authority, "it expresses repentance; in this connection it is one of the emblems of the Passion." The placing of the image of a cock on church towers is said to be an allusion to Peter as the head of the Church on earth, and as representing the voice of the Church, which by day and in the watches

of the night calls on men to repent. Another tradition
is that some early pope ordered that the weathervane on
churches be in that form in order to remind the clergy of
the necessity of watchfulness—a second reference to
Mark, iii, 35.

Ragozin tells us that in the *Vendida,* the "Bible" of the
ancient Medes, great credit is given to the cock as the
messenger who calls men to the performance of their
religious duties: "Arise, O men! Whichever first gets
up shall enter paradise!" A Hebrew legendary saying
is that when a cock crows before dawn it warns: "Remember thy Creator, O thoughtless man!" Finally
Drayton sings of—

> The cock, the country horologe that rings
> The cheerful warning to the sun's awake.

Nowadays, if chanticleer calls to mind anything in
particular, except wrath at his too early rising to adore
the god of day, it is the spirit of boastfulness and "cock-
sureness"; while his humble mate represents maternal
cares carried to the extreme of fussiness.

The names of a good many birds serve as synonyms of
prevailing ideas, or become figures of speech, without
having a special myth or story behind them. Thus the
words *eagle* and *falcon* convey to the listener the notion
of nobility in power, while *hawk* simply means fierceness,
with somewhat of prying, detective skill. *Owl* provokes
in the imagination a rather smiling picture of solemn
pretence of wisdom—a reputation, by the way, almost
wholly due to the little European screech-owl's accidental
association with Pallas Athene. *Swallow* suggests spring
all over the world; *goose* and *gull* connote easy credulity
and foolishness; *vulture* and *raven,* rapine and cruelty;

parrot senseless chatter or the lavish repetition of another's ideas or sayings; *cuckoo*, poaching on another
man's domestic preserves; and so on down to the *stork*,
which in Germany symbolizes filial piety because of its
fancied solicitude toward aged storks, and which children
are taught to believe brings babies from the fountain to
their mothers' laps. The Chinese and Japanese peasantry
hold the *Mandarin duck* in high esteem as a model of
conjugal virtues, because it is said to mate for life, and
Hindoos feel the same toward their (sarus) *crane*—a
bird that figures extensively in the legendary lore of both
China and Japan. Figures of the crane are found deco-
rating bridal attire in Japan, and this bird is commended
to womankind generally in Nippon as an example of
motherhood to be emulated. "In this respect it is like
the *pheasant*, which is said to stay by her young during
a grass-fire, covering them with her outstretched wings
until, together, they perish in the flames; for in a similar
way the crane shields her young from the bitter cold of
the winter snows."

In ancient Egypt the plume of the *ostrich*, "on account
of the mathematical equality of the opposing barbs in
point of length—a peculiarity not present in the primary
feathers of any other bird with which the Egyptians were
acquainted—was regarded as the sacred symbol of justice."
Osiris was represented with two ostrich plumes in his
crown. Says Dr. Cyrus Adler: "The Egyptian considered the *hoopoe* as symbolical of gratitude because it
repays the early kindness of its parents in their old age
by trimming their wings and bringing them food when
they are acquiring new plumage. The Arabs call it
'doctor,' believing it to possess marvellous medicinal
qualities, and they use its head in charms and incanta-
tions."

CHAPTER VIII

BLACK FEATHERS MAKE BLACK BIRDS

NO one bird known to Americans is so entangled with whatever witchcraft belongs to birds as is the raven, yet little of it is American besides Poe's melodramatic mummery, whose raven was a borrowed piece of theatrical property. The shrewd people of this country pay little attention to signs and portents, yet some survive among us, for the extravagant notions popularly held as to the sagacity of our crow, with its "courts" and "consultations," are no doubt traceable in some measure to the bird's history in Old World superstition.

In Europe no bird, save possibly the cuckoo, is so laden with legends and superstitious veneration as the raven, chiefly, however, in the North, where it is not only most numerous and noticeable but seems to fit better than in the gladsome South. To the rough, virile Baltic man, or to the Himalayan mountaineer, worshipping force, careless of beauty, this sable bird of hard endurance, challenging cry and powerful wing, the "ravener," tearer, was an admirable creature; while to the more esthetic dweller by the Mediterranean or on Ægean shores such qualities were repulsive, and the raven became a reminder of winter, when alone it was seen in the South, and of the savage forests and hated barbarians whence it came. Much the same antithesis belongs to this bird and its relatives in the minds of Orientals. To understand the impression the raven made on primitive men, and the symbolism and dread that have grown up about it, one must have some knowledge of the real *Corvus corax*.

The raven is the largest member of the ornithological family Corvidæ, measuring two feet from beak to tail-tip. It is everywhere black, with steel-blue and purplish reflections, and is distinguished from its equally black cousins, the crows, by its stouter beak, somewhat hooked at the tip, and especially by the elongated and pointed feathers on the throat. It is powerful in flight, and is noted for performing queer antics in the air. Judged by its anatomy it stands high in the scale of classification, so that some ornithologists, considering also its intellect, have put it quite at the top of the scale—made it the true King of Birds. In its northern home this species is to be found right around the world, inhabiting Asia and Europe as far south as the great ridge of mountains that extends from Spain to Siberia, and also living in Asia Minor and Syria. It is native to all North America, where no arctic island is too remote to be visited by it in summer. Most of the ravens fly southward in winter from polar latitudes to kindlier regions, but those that stay in the far north become doubly conspicuous in a wilderness of snow, for they do not turn white in winter as do many arctic residents; therefore Goldsmith wasted much philosophy in explaining in his *Animated Nature* why they "become white." The raven's ordinary call-note is well enough described by the words "croak" and "caw," but it has many variations. Nuttall quotes Porphyrius as declaring that no less than 64 different intonations of the raven's cries were distinguished by the sooth-sayers of his day, and given appropriate significance. Some notes are indescribably queer.

Ravens have almost disappeared from thickly settled

regions, in striking contrast to their near relatives the
crows, rooks, choughs, magpies, jackdaws, and various
related species in the Old World, which thrive and grow
tame in the company of civilized humanity. Few pairs
of ravens remain in the United States east of the Rocky
Mountains, except on the wilder parts of the Maine coast
and about Lake Superior.

Readers of Charles Dickens's novels will recall the imp-
ish specimen "Grip" that Barnaby Rudge used to carry
about with him, and which became his fellow-prisoner in
jail—and served him right, for he was always declaring
"I'm a devil!"

This raven was modelled after an actual pet, named
"Grip," in the family of the novelist when he was writing *Barnaby Rudge* in 1841. It died in July of that year,
and its body passed into the possession of Dr. R. T. Judd,
an English collector of Dickens' material. In 1922 this
collection, including the stuffed skin of Grip, and its
former cage, labelled with its owner's name, was offered
for sale at the Anderson Galleries in New York. It appears from accompanying letters that as the novel was
originally written it contained no reference to the bird;
but before the manuscript was completed it occurred to
Mr. Dickens that he could make good use of the mischievous creature in the story, as is revealed in a letter
to George Cattermole, dated January 28, 1841.

The raven may not only be tamed to the point of
domestication, but will learn to speak a few words. Goldsmith asserted, apparently from experience, that it not
only would speak but could "sing like a man." Like all
its thievish tribe it loves to pick up and hide objects that
attract its quick eye, especially if they are bright, like
a silver spoon or a bit of jewelry; and this acquisitive

disposition has more than once involved in serious misfortune servants accused of purloining lost articles, as happened in the case of the Jackdaw of Rheims.

The tradition on which Barham's *Ingoldsby Legend* is embroidered is a very old one, the earliest statement of which, probably, is that in Mignie's *Patrologia Latinia,* compiled by a monk of Clairvaux. The narrative is that of an incident in the time of Frederick Barbarossa (12th century) when the monastery of Corvey was ruled by a prince-bishop named Conrad. One day he left his episcopal ring lying on the dining-table, and it disappeared. The bishop blamed the servants and suspected his guests, and finally issued a decree of excommunication toward any one who had stolen it. Thereupon the bishop's pet jackdaw "began to sicken little by little, to loathe his food, to cease more and more from his droll croakings and irrational follies whereby he was wont to delight the minds of fools who neglect to fear God."

At this dreadful stage it occurred to some bright genius that this portentous change in the bird was the effect of the curse, and that it was the sought-for thief. Its nest was searched, the precious ring was found, the curse was taken off, and the jackdaw recovered its plumage and good spirits.

Where ravens can get other food plentifully they seldom attack living animals. Bendire frequently saw them feeding among his chickens without harming them, yet undoubtedly they are occasionally guilty in our West of killing young lambs, game-birds, and poultry, sins of which they are much accused in Europe. Certainly they rob wild birds of eggs and fledglings, but these evil deeds are done mainly in spring, in providing their own nestlings with soft food. During most of the year the food of the raven consists of carrion, grasshoppers, worms, mussels and other shellfish (the larger kinds of which they lift high in the air and then drop to break their shells), and of ground-squirrels and young rabbits when they can get hold of them.

When a raven alights on a dead animal its first act is to pluck out the eyes. One of the barbarities in the ancient East was to throw the bodies of executed criminals out to be devoured by beasts and birds of prey—a custom of which the Parsee Towers of Silence is a modified relic. The popular knowledge of this gave great force to Solomon's warning (*Proverbs* xxx, 17): "The eye that mocketh at his father, and despiseth to obey his mother, the ravens of the valley shall pick it out"—that is, so bad a boy would end on the gallows.

Although ravens were regarded by the ancient Zoroastrians as "pure," because they were considered necessary to remove pollution from the face of the earth, the Jews classed this creature as "unclean" for the same reason—it ate carrion. In view of this the Biblical legend that the Prophet Elijah, when he hid by the brook Kerith from the wrath of Ahab, was fed by ravens at command of the Lord, is so unnatural that commentators have done their best to explain it away. To this day the Moors regard ravens as belonging to Satan. In Chapter V of the *Koran,* where the killing of Cain by his brother is described, we read: "And God sent a raven which scratched the earth to show him how he should hide the shame [that is, the corpse] of his brother, and he said 'Woe is me! am I to be like this raven?' . . . and he became one of those who repent." This is from Sale's edition, Philadelphia, 1868; and the editor adds a note that this legend was derived from the Jews, but that in their version the raven appears not to Cain but to Adam, who thereupon buried Abel.

That a bird black as night and its mysteries, a familiar of the lightning-riven pine and the storm-beaten crag, a ghoulish attendant of battling men and feasting on their slain, muttering strange soliloquies, and diabolically cunning withal—that such a creature should have appealed to the rough mariners of the North is far from surprising. The supreme Norse god was Odin, an impersonation of force and intellect—an apotheosis, indeed, of the Viking himself; and his ministers were two ravens, Hugin and Munin, *i.e.,* Reflection and Memory. "They sit upon his shoulders and whisper in his ears," says history. "He sends them out at daybreak to fly over the world, and they come back at eve, toward meal-time." Hence it is that Odin knows so much, and is called *Rafnagud,* Raven-god. Most solicitously does Odin express himself about these ministers in Grunner's lay in the *Elder Edda*:

> Hugin and Munin fly each day
> Over the spacious earth. I fear for Hugin
> That he come not back,
> Yet more anxious am I for Munin.

Again, in Odin's fierce *Raven Song,* Hugin goes "to explore the heavens." Jupiter's two eagles, sent east and west, will be recalled by readers of classic tales.

As the eagle of Jove became the standard of the Roman legions, so Odin's bird was inscribed on the shields and the banners of his warrior sons. You may see such banners illustrated in the Bayeux tapestry. The Dane called his standard *landeyda* (land-waster), and had faith in its miraculous virtues. The original ensign, that is, the one brought to England by the first invaders, is described in St. Neot's biographical *Chronicles* (9th century). In 878, it records, a wild Danish rover named Hubba came with twenty-three ships on a raid into Devon: but the people rose and killed or drove away all the vikings.

"And there got they [that is, the Devon men] no small spoil, wherein they took, moreover, that banner which men call the Raven. For they say that the three sisters of Ingwar and Hubba, the daughters, sooth to say, of Lodbrock, wove that banner, and made it all wholly ready between morn and night of a single day. They say, too, that in every fight wherein that flag went before them, if they were to win the raven in the midst thereof seemed to flutter, as if it were alive, but were their doom to be worsted, then it would droop, still and lifeless."

Britain came to know well that portentous flag—

> The Danish raven, lured by annual prey,
> Hung o'er the land incessant,

as Thomson laments. Finally Harold hurled the power of Canute from England's shores forever, and Tennyson sings Harold's paean:

> We have shattered back
> The hugest wave from Norseland ever yet
> Surged on us, and our battle-axes broken
> The Raven's wing, and dumbed the carrion croak
> From the gray sea forever.

"The crow and the raven," MacBain [71] announces, "are constantly connected in the Northern mythologies with battle-deities. 'How is it with you, Ravens?' says the Norse *Raven Song*. 'Whence are you come with gory beak at the dawning of the day. . . . You lodged last

night, I ween, where ye knew the corses were lying.'
The ravens also assist and protect heroes both in Irish
and Norse myth. It was a lucky sign if a raven followed
a warrior."

But the bold Norse sailors made a more practical use
also of this knowing bird, for in those days, before the
compass, they used to take ravens with them in their
adventurous voyages on the fog-bound northern seas,
and trust the birds to show them the way back to land.
A notable instance was Floki's voyage to Iceland in 864
A. D., a few years after that island's discovery; and the
French historian Mallet [30] narrates it thus:

We are told that Floki, previous to setting out on his expedition, performed a great sacrifice, and having consecrated three
ravens to the gods took them with him to guide him on his
voyage. After touching at the Shetland and Faroë islands he
steered northwest, and when he was fairly out at sea, let loose
one of his ravens, which, after rising to a considerable elevation.
directed its flight to the land they had quitted. . . . The second
bird, after being some time on the wing, returned to the ship,
a sign that the land was too far distant to be descried even by
a raven hovering in the sky. Floki therefore continued his
course, and shortly afterwards let loose his third raven, which
he followed in its flight until he reached the eastern coast of
Iceland.

This is a somewhat poetic account, I imagine, of what
perhaps was a more prosaic custom of seamanship, for
doubtless it was usual at that time to carry several birds
on such voyages, and to let them fly from time to time
that they might learn and indicate to the voyagers
whether land was near, and in what direction, as did old
Captain Noah, master of the good ship *Ark*. Berthold

Lauffer[52] treats of this point with his customary thoroughness in his pamphlet *Bird Divination:*

Indian Hindoo navigators kept birds on board ship for the purpose of despatching them in search of land. In the *Baveru-Jataka* it is "a crow serving to direct navigators in the four quarters" . . . Pliny relates that the seafarers of Taprobane (Ceylon) did not observe the stars for the purpose of navigation, but carried birds out to sea, which they sent off from time to time and then followed the course of the birds' flying in the direction of the land. The connection of this practice with that described in the Babylonian and Hebraic traditions of the deluge was long ago recognized. . . . When the people of Thera, an island in the Ægean Sea emigrated to Libya, ravens flew along with them ahead of the ships to show the way. According to Justin . . . it was by the flight of birds that the Gauls who invaded Illyricum were guided. Emperor Jimmu of Japan (7th century) engaged in a war expedition and marched under the guidance of a gold-colored raven.

Mr. Lauffer might have added that Callisthenes relates that two heaven-sent ravens led the expedition of Alexander across the trackless desert from the Mediterranean coast to the oasis of Ammon (Siwah), recalling stragglers now and then by hoarse croaking.

The folklore of northern Europe is full of the cunning and exploits of this bird and its congeners, which it would be a weary task to disentangle from pure myth. In Germany there is, or was, a stone gibbet called, with gruesome memories, Ravenstone, to which Byron alludes in *Werner*—

> Do you think
> I'll honor you so much as save your throat
> From the Ravenstone by choking myself?

We read that the old Welsh king Owein, son of Urien, had in his army three hundred doughty ravens, constituting an irresistible force; perhaps they were only human "shock" troops who bore this device on their targes. Cuchulain, the savage hero of Irish fables, had, like Odin, two magic ravens that advised him of the approach of foes. Old-fashioned Germans believe that Frederick I (Barbarossa) is sleeping under Raven's Hill at Kaiserlauten, ready to come forth in the last emergency of his country. There in his grotto-palace a shepherd found him sleeping. Barbarossa awoke and asked: "Are the ravens still flying around the hill?" The shepherd answered that they were. "Then," sighed the king, "I must sleep another hundred years."

Waterton [73] tells us that a tradition was once current throughout the whole of Great Britain that King Arthur was changed into a raven (some say a chough) by the art of witchcraft; and that in due time he would be restored to human form, and return with crown and sceptre. In Brittany, where Arthur and his knights are much more real even in Cornwall, the sailor-peasants will assure you that he was buried on the little isle of Avalon, just off the foreshore of Tregastel, but they will add very seriously that he is not dead. If you inquire how that can be, they will explain that the great king was conveyed thither magically by Morgan le Fay, and he and she dwell there in an underground palace. They are invisible now to all human eyes, and when Arthur wants to go out into the air his companion turns him into a raven; and perchance, in proof, your boatman may point your gaze toward a real raven sitting on the rocks of the islet.

Ravens figure in many monkish legends, too, usually in a beneficent attitude, in remembrance of their friendly offices toward Elijah. Saint Cuthbert and several lesser saints and hermits were fed by these or similar birds.

One hermit subsisted many years on a daily ration of
half a loaf of bread brought him by a raven, and one
time, when another saint visited him, the bird provided a whole loaf! Fish was frequently brought: and
once when a certain eremite was ill, the bird furnished
the fish already cooked, and fed it to the patient bit by
bit. Miss Walker [39] shows that as a companion of saints
this bird has had a wide and beneficent experience, which
may be set against the more conspicuous pages of mis-
deeds in his highly variegated record. Thus we learn
that St. Benedict's raven saved his life by bearing away
the poisoned loaf sent to this saint by a jealous priest.
"After his torture and death at Saragossa, when the body
of St. Vincent was thrown to the wild beasts it was rescued by ravens and borne to his brothers at Valencia,
where it reposed in a tomb till the Christians of that place
were expelled by the Moors. The remains of the saint
were . . . again placed in a tomb [at Cape St. Vincent]
to be guarded forever more by the faithful ravens."
Have you doubts about this story? Go to that wild head-
land, where Portugal sets a firm foot against the Atlantic,
watch the ravens hovering above it, and be convinced!
And to many other holy men did these noble birds render
substantial service—to St. Meinrad especially, as is
affirmed by no less an authority than the great Jerome.

"In some parts of Germany," Miss Walker records,
"these birds are believed to hold the souls of the damned,
while in other sections wicked priests only are supposed
to be so re-incarnated. In Sweden the ravens croaking
at night in the swamps are said to be the ghosts of murdered persons who have been denied Christian burial."
A local and humorous touch is given to this conception
by the Irish in Kerry, who allege that the rooks there

are the ghosts of bad old landlords, because they steal vegetables from the peasants' gardens—"Always robbin' the poor!"

This eerie feeling is of long descent. The supreme war-goddess of the Gaels, as Squire [74] explains, was Morrigu, the Red Woman or war-goddess, who figures in the adventures of Cuchulain, and whose favorite disguise was to change herself into a carrion-crow, the "hoodie-crow" of the Scotch. She had assistants who revelled among the slain on a battlefield. "These grim creatures of the savage mind had immense vitality . . . indeed, they may be said to survive still in the superstitious dislike and suspicion shown in all Keltic-speaking countries for their avatar—the hoodie crow."

In Pennant's *Tour in Scotland* (1771) is described a curious ceremony in which offerings were made by Scottish herdsmen to the hooded crow, eagle and other enemies of sheep to induce them to spare the flocks. A Morayshire saying in old times ran thus:

> The guil, the Gordon, and the hoodie crow,
> Were the three worst things Murray ever saw.

(The guil, Swann explains, is an obnoxious weed, the Gordon refers to the thieving propensities of a neighboring clan, and the crow killed lambs and annoyed sickly sheep.) "It is interesting," says Wentz,[62] "to observe that this Irish war-goddess Morrigu, the *bodb* or *babd,* . . . has survived to our own day in the fairy-lore of the chief Celtic countries. In Ireland the survival in the popular and still almost general belief among the peasantry that the fairies often exercise their magical powers under the form of royston crows; and for this reason these birds are always greatly dreaded and avoided. The resting of one of them on a peasant's cottage may signify many things, but often it means the death of one of the family or some great misfortune, the bird in such case playing the part of a *bean-sidhe* (banshee)" In the western Highlands "the hoody crow plays the same rôle; and in Brittany fairies assume the form of the magpie."

Under the influence of Christian teaching Odin gradually became identified throughout northern Europe with Satan: so the raven and all the Corvidae are now "Devil's birds" in the folklore of the North. Even the magpie is said to have devils' blood in its tongue, and its chattering is ominous of evil, requiring various rustic charms to counteract its harm—in fact, if the farmer-folk are correctly informed, virtually all the birds of this family was naturally tainted with deviltry. It is not surprising then to hear that European crows go down to hell once every year, when they must appear before Old Nick and give him a tribute of feathers. The time of this visit coincides with their moulting-season in midsummer, when the crows retire and remain inconspicuous and silent for a time—so maybe it's true!

An extraordinary survival of this last notion—unless it be original—is found among the negroes of some of our Southern States, who say that the "jaybird" (blue-jay) is never to be seen on Friday, because on that day he is carrying sticks to the Devil in hell; that in general this bird is the Devil's messenger and spy; and that the reason he is so gay and noisy on Saturday is that he is so glad to get back to earth. An old Georgia darky explained the matter a follows:

"Some folks say Br'er Jay takes a piece er wood, des a splinter, down to de bad Place ev'y Friday fer ter help out

Mister Devil, so's to let him 'n' his wife, ole Aunty Squatty, have good kindlin' wood all de time. . . . But some folks tell de tale 'nother way. Dey say he make dat trip ever' Friday ter tote down des a grit er dirt. He make de trip sho'. Ever'body knows dat. But for what he goes folks tells diffunt tales. You sho'ly can't see a jay bird in dis worl' on Friday fum twelve o'clock twel three—hit takes 'em des dat long ter make de trip. . . . Some folks say Bre'r Jay and all his fambly, his folks, his cousins, and his kin, does go dat way and d'rection, ev'y one totin' dey grain o' sand in der bill an' drappin' hit in— des one teeny weeny grit—wid de good hopes er fillin' up dat awful place."[2]

Lousiana negroes are of the opinion that the jay is condemned to this weekly trip as a punishment for misbehavior at Christ's crucifixion, but what dreadful deed he did has been forgotten. Every reader of "Uncle Remus," or of the stories of Mrs. Ruth McEnery Stuart, Mr. Harry Stillwell Edwards, and other Southern writers, knows how largely the "jaybird" figures in the plantation-tales of the negroes, especially of the coastal districts, where the bluejay is one of the most conspicuous and interesting of resident birds.

The coming of Christianity, as has been said, swept away the images of Odin and of his Pagan familiars Hugin and Munin out of both Teutonic and Keltic Europe, but it did not sweep away the birds themselves, nor discolor their sable wings, nor silence the baleful croak; and the impression left by the old tales lingered long in the minds of the people. To the horror of the raven and his kind among the natives of Britain, as a symbol of the northern marauders from whom they had so long suffered, was now added the anathema of pious missionaries who condemned everything pagan as diabolic, and all things black—except their own robes— as typifying the powers of darkness. Truly, remarked

St. Ambrose, all shamelessness and sin are dark and gloomy, and feed on the dead like the crow. A Chinese epithet for the raven is "Mongols' coffin."

The people were sincere enough in this, for behind them was not only the Devil-fearing superstition of the Middle Ages but a long line of parent myths and folklore that made the bird's reputation as black as its plumage, and added to this was the new and terrifying idea of prophecy. You get a hint of the feeling in Gower's *Confessio Amantis:*

> A Raven by whom yet men maie
> Take evidence, when he crieth,
> That some mishap it signifieth.

In Greece and Italy ravens were sacred to Apollo, the great patron of augurs, who in a pet turned this bird from white to black—and an ill turn it was, *for black feathers make black birds;* and in this blackness of coat lies, in my opinion, the root of their sinister repute.

The "jumbie-bird," or "big witch," of the West Indian region, for example, is the dead-black ani, a kind of cuckoo. Spenser speaks of "the hoarse night-raven, trompe of doleful dreer," but his "night-raven" was not a raven at all, but the bittern.

It is only in an earlier day and under a brighter sky that we find these corvine prophets taking a more cheerful view of the future. Of course they are among the "rain-birds":

> Hark
> How the curst raven with his harmless voice
> Invokes the rain.

So the "foresight of a raven" became proverbial, as

Waterton [73] illustrates by an anecdote: "Good farmer Muckdrag's wife, while jogging on with eggs to market, knew there was mischief brewing as soon as she had heard a raven croak on the unlucky side of the road:

> "That raven on the left-hand oak,
> Curse on his ill-betiding croak,
> Bodes me no good!"

She had scarcely uttered this when down came her old stumbling mare to the ground. Her every egg was smashed to atoms; and whilst she lay sprawling . . . she was perfectly convinced in her own mind that the raven had clearly foreseen her irreparable misadventure."

If one alighted on a church-tower the whole parish trembled, and when a cottager saw one perched on his roof-tree he made his will; or if it happened that a man or woman was ill in his house the death of that person was regarded as certain. The more learned would quote for you how Tiberius, Plato, Cicero and other great men of the past had been similarly warned, and doubtless many a person has died in these circumstances of nervous fright and discouragement. It is to this dread that Marlowe refers in his *Jew of Malta:*

> Like the sad presaging raven that tolls
> The sick man's passport in her hollow beak,
> And, in the shadow of the silent night,
> Does shake contagion from her sable wing.

The last line contains a new and heinous calumny widely credited. So Shakespeare makes Caliban threaten Prospero and Ariel with

> As wicked dew as e'er my mother brushed
> With raven's feather from unwholesome fen.

I wonder, by the way, who first spoke—the simile is, at any rate, as old as Chaucer's time—of the wrinkles that gather about the corners of our eyes when we get on in life, as "crow's feet"? Frederick Locker sings of his grandmother:

> Her locks as white as snow,
> Once shamed the swarthy crow;
>   By-and-by
> That fowl's avenging sprite
> Set his cruel foot for spite
>   Near her eye.

The expression of course is a suggestion of the radiating form of the wrinkles at the outer corner of the eye to a crow's track; and this reminds us of the fact that when soon after the Norman conquest in England there was a vast popular interest in royal genealogy, people spoke of the branching form of a family tree, when drawn on paper, as a "crane's foot" (*pied de grue*), whence our term *pedigree*.

Omens are deduced from the flight and cries of ravens, crows, magpies, and certain other corvine species, especially as regards their direction relative to the inquirer. Horace, for example, in his *Ode to Galatea* on her undertaking a journey, tells her that he, as a "provident augur,"

> Ere the wierd crow, re-seeking stagnant marshes,
> Predict the rainstorm, will invoke the raven
> From the far East, who, as the priestlier croaker,
>   Shall overawe him.

That is to say, Horace will make the raven, appearing or heard from the eastward (the lucky direction), over-rule the bad omen of the crow.

There is also grave meaning in the number visible at
one time, as Matthew Lewis knew when he wrote the
ballad *Bill Jones:*

"Ah, well-a-day," the sailor said,
   "Some danger must impend,
Three ravens sit in yonder glade,
And evil will happen I'm sore afraid
   Ere we reach our journey's end."

"And what have the ravens with us to do?
   Does their sight betoken us evil?"
"To see one raven is luck, 'tis true,
  But it's certain misfortune to light upon two,
   And meeting with three is the devil."

Quoting Margaret Walker: [39]

The belief in his power of divination was so general that
knowledge of the whereabouts of the lost has come to be known
as "raven's knowledge." To the Romans he was able to reveal
the means of restoring lost eyesight even. In Germany he was
able to tell not only where lost articles were, but could also
make known to survivors where the souls of their lost friends
were to be found. In Bohemia he was assigned the task usually
performed by the stork in other lands, while in some parts
of Germany witches were credited with riding upon his back instead of on the conventional broomstick.

Regular formulas regarding magpies are repeated in
rural Britain, where magpies are numerous—they are
common in our American West, also, but nobody is superstitious about them there—of which a common example
runs:

     One for sorrow, two for mirth,
     Three for a wedding, four for a birth.

Many variations of these formulas are on record, some
carrying the rimes up to eight or nine pies seen at once;

and folklore has many quaint ways of dissipating the evil effects feared from their presence.

Now all this is but the ragtag and bobtail, as it were, of the *science* of the ancient Oriental world that has come down to us in frayed and disconnected fragments, to be now a matter more of amusing research than of belief or practice among most of us. It was old even at the beginning of the Christian era, but all the ornithomancy of the Greek and Roman soothsayers was inherited in its principle, if not always in its forms, from the remotely antique "wisdom" of the East, in which the consultation of birds appears to be the basis of divination.

In the Far East the raven has been regarded from time immemorial with dread interest, and where that species was rare the crow—equally black, destructive, and cunning—took its place. To the primitive philosophers of Persia and India the raven was a divine bird, of celestial origin and supernatural abilities, and was the messenger who announced the will of the Deity. A German commentator on the *Vedas,* H. Oldenberg, concludes that the animals sent by the gods, as pictured in the myths, were those of a weird, demoniacal nature, and were for this reason themselves deified, but subsequently became mere stewards to divine mandators. "In the belief of the Persians," says Lauffer, "the raven was sacred to the god of light and the sun." Moncure D. Conway,[56] when discussing the Biblical legend of the Deluge, suggests that the raven sent out of the Ark may typify the "darkness of the face of the deep," and the dove the "spirit of God" that "moved upon the face of the waters."

In China, Dr. Williams [76] tells us, "the sun is signalized by the figure of a raven in a circle." I have seen Chinese drawings of it in which the raven (or a crow) stood on

three legs, as does the toad that the Taoists see in the
moon—but why three legs? Mrs. Ball answers this
question thus:

The crow—known in China as *wuya,* and in Japan as *karasu*
—is most intimately related to the sun. Ch'un Ch'iu in an
ancient poem says: "The spirit of the sun is a crow with three
legs"; while again Hwai Nan Tse, an ancient philosopher, explains that this crow has three legs because the number three
is the emblem of *yang* [light, good] of which the sun is the
supreme essence. . . . The Chinese, it would appear, actually
believed in the existence of a three-legged crow, for in the
official history of the Wei dynasty—3d century A. D.—it is
related that "more than thirty times, tributes consisting of three-
legged crows were brought from the neighboring countries.
. . . The principal of sun-worship [in Japan] was Amateresv
no Ohokami, from whom the imperial family traces its descent.
This divinity . . . had as her messenger and attendant . . . a
red bird having three legs."

Based on the fears and philosophy indicated above, the
soothsayers of India contrived a most elaborate scheme
of judging meanings from the actions of ravens and
crows, for little attention seems to have been paid to
ornithological distinctions; and this spread in very early
times to China and Thibet. It is a wonderful monument
of priestcraft, which has been elucidated by several
students of early Oriental manuscripts; and I am in-
debted to a profoundly learned discourse on the subject
by Dr. Berthold Lauffer.[52] Briefly the scheme was as
follows:

A table or chart was constructed containing ninety
squares, each square holding an interpretation of one or
another sound of a raven's or crow's voice; but his
utterances were separated into five characters of sound,
and the day divided into five "watches," while the direction from which the bird's voice came may be from any

one of eight points of the compass, or from the zenith, making nine points in all. Multiplying these together gives the ninety squares of the mystic table, and the intersection of two conditions gives you the square where the appropriate interpretation or prophecy is written.

Thus if in the first watch (*i.e.,* early in the morning) you hear a raven in the east say *ka-ka,* your wish to obtain more property will be fulfilled; but if in the fourth watch you hear a bird off in the southeast say *da-da* you may be sure that a storm will arise in seven days. Five different tones of the cawing were recognized as significant. Just where and what you see a raven do when you are travelling foretells some sort of a fortunate or unfortunate incident of the progress or outcome of your journey; yet these omens differ according to whether you are moving and the bird is stationary, or you are standing still and the bird is flying, or both or neither are motionless!

There was also a settled rule for taking prognostications from the nests of these birds. "When a crow has built its nest on a branch on the east side of a tree," according to Donacila's translation of a Thibetan manuscript, "a good year and rain will be the result of it. When it has built its nest on a southern branch the crops will then be bad. When it has built its nest on a branch in the middle of a tree, a great fright will then be the result of it. When it makes its nest below, fear of the army of one's adversary will be the result of it. When it makes its nest on a wall, on the ground, or on a river, the [sick] king will be healed."

Whenever it appears that the omen observed portends harm, offerings of food and so forth must be made to the bird in order to avert the evil, and these offerings vary according to prescribed rules. It is no wonder that an extensive priesthood was needed to aid in this intricate guarding against danger or the foretelling of benefits to come; and one suspects that the whole thing was a clever invention by the sacerdotal class to provide priests with a good living. Nor have the practices, and much less the superstitious notions behind them, become wholly obsolete, for not only in India and China are the movements of birds now watched with anxiety, and offerings made to them in the temples and individually by the peasantry, but similar ideas and practices prevail in all Malayan lands, as readers of such books as Skeat's *Malay Magic* ⁷ may learn.

Perhaps learned students of ancient ways of thinking may be able to explain why the *direction* of a prophetic bird from the listener was an essential element in its message: for example, why is the cawing of a crow east of you a more favorable portent than cawing from the west? Lord Lytton studies this question briefly in the Notes to his translation of the *Odes* of Horace, who, in his Ode to Galatea, exclaims:

> May no chough's dark shadow
> Lose thee a sunbeam, nor one green woodpecker
> Dare to tap leftward.

Why should "leftward" (*lævus*) signify ill-luck in this case, when the left was considered lucky by the Romans, although unlucky by the Greeks? "It is suggested," is Lytton's comment, "that the comparison may have arisen from the different practice of the Greeks and Romans in taking note of birds—the former facing north, the latter south [an attitude connected with migration?] I believe, however, it was the tap of the woodpecker, and not his flight, that was unlucky. It is so considered still in Italy, and corresponds to our superstitious fear of the beetle called the death-watch. If, therefore, heard on the left, or heart side, it directly menaced life."

I leave the solution of the general problem of the value of direction in ancient ornithomancy to the Orientalists, advising them that a hint of subtile and half-forgotten reasons for such distinctions may be found in the ideas prevailing among the shamans, or "medicine men," of our southwestern village-Indians; among the Hopi (miscalled Mokis), for example, North is represented in their mystical ceremonies by yellow, West by blue, South by red, and East by white.

Religious interest in black-hued birds is not confined to the Old World, as was tragically illustrated in that remarkable excitement among the Indians of the Upper Missouri region in 1890, known as the Ghost Dance, of which the crow was the honored symbol. James Mooney,[77] of the United States Bureau of Ethnology, investigated this outburst of sentiment very thoroughly, and explained it at length in the 14th Annual Report of that Bureau, from which I extract the information as to the crow's part in the matter. Dr. Mooney reminds us in advance that the crow was probably held sacred by all the tribes of the Algonquian race. Roger Williams, speaking of the New England tribes, says that although the crow did damage to the corn, hardly an Indian would kill one, because it was their tradition that this bird had brought them their first grain and vegetables, "carrying a grain of corn in one ear and a bean in the other from the field of their great god Cautantouwit in Sowwaniu, the Southwest, the happy spirit-world where dwelt the gods and the souls of the great and good."

The so-called Ghost Dance meant to the Plains Indians generally a preparation for the coming of a superhuman Messiah who would restore the old order of things when the redman was supreme in the land, and free from the restraint of an alien and encroaching civilization; and primarily it contained no special hostility toward white neighbors.

Among the western redmen the eagle for its general superiority, the magpie (particularly by the Paiutes), the sagehen because connected with the country whence the Messiah was to come, and some other birds, were revered in certain subsidiary ceremonies; but the central bird-figure in this excitement was the crow, for it was regarded as the directing messenger from the spirit-world, because its color is a reminder of death and the shadow-land. I have seen the figures of two upward flying crows and two magpies in a "medicine shirt" made to be worn in the Ghost Dance. The raven shared in this devotional respect, but is rare on the northern plains, where its humbler relative was an abundant substitute. Some understanding of this supreme position of the crow in the Ghost-dancing—the equivalent of our "revival" meetings—may be had by examining the Arapahoe version of the belief on which the anticipated advent of a red Messiah was based. Dr. Mooney expounds it [77] as follows:

In Arapahoe belief the spirit world is in the west, not on the same level with this earth of ours, but higher up, and separated also from it by a body of water. . . . The crow, as the messenger and leader of the spirits who had gone before [i.e. the dead] collected their armies on the other side and advanced at their head to the hither limit of the shadow-land. Then, looking over, they saw far below them a sea, and far out beyond it toward the east was the boundary of the earth, where lived the friends they were marching to rejoin. Taking up a pebble in his beak, the crow then dropped it into the water and it became a mountain towering up to the land of the dead. Down its rocky slope he brought his army until they halted at the edge of the water. Then taking some dust in his bill the crow flew out and dropped it into the water as he flew, and it became a solid arm of land stretching from the spirit world to the earth. He returned and flew out again, this time with some blades of grass, which he dropped upon the land thus made and at once it was covered with a green sod. Again he returned and again flew out, this time with some twigs in his bill, and dropping these also upon the new land, at once it was covered with a forest of trees. Again he flew back to the base of the mountain, and is now [that is, at the time of the Ghost dancing] coming on at the head of all the countless spirit-host.

CHAPTER IX

THE FAMILIAR OF WITCHES

I FEAR no one would admit that a book of this character was anywhere near complete did it not include at least one chapter on the observances and superstitions connected with owls. Nevertheless I doubt whether I should not have taken the risk of the reader's displeasure had I not been able to avail myself of essays by several men who have handled this large and intricate phase of bird-lore in a way that discourages any rivalry.

The Atlantic Monthly for September, 1874, contained an article by Alexander Young on "Birds of Ill omen," in which one may find treated not only the historic dread of owls, but many similar facts and fears connected with ravens, crows, magpies, and their fellow-craftsmen in alleged diabolism. "Most birds," Mr. Young remarks, "were considered ominous of good or evil according to the place and manner of their appearance. . . . It is noticeable that this stigma has been affixed only to those birds whose appearance or voice is disagreeable, and whose habits are somewhat peculiar." The nocturnal owls perhaps fulfil these conditions as well as any bird could. "Their retired habits," to quote Broderip,[78] "the desolate places that are their favorite haunts, their hollow hootings, fearful shrieks, serpent-like hissings and coffin-maker-like snappings, have helped to give them a bad eminence, more than overbalancing all the glory that Minerva and her own Athens could shed around them."

The little Grecian owl—it is a foreign replica of our
own small screech owl, which, as a matter of fact, gurgles
rather melodiously instead of screeching—was well
thought of in Athens in its prime, and was the special
cognizance of the wise and dignified goddess of her
citizens, Pallas Athene—Minerva of the Romans. De
Kay,[18] indeed, reasons her out an owl-goddess, and it is
said that statues of her have been found with an owl's instead of a human head. If she was a humanized expression for the moon, as some interpret her, this little
lover of moonlight is most suitable as her symbol. Therefore one need not speculate on the reputed "wisdom" of
the owl, any owl—said to be proved wise by its being the
only bird that looks straight before it—for that reputation is merely a reflection from the attributes of its
patron, the stately goddess. Homer makes Athene the
special protector of those, chiefly women, engaged in
textile crafts; and there is an old saying that the owl was
a weaver's daughter, spinning with silver threads. When,
therefore, in the midst of the momentous naval battle of
Salamis an owl alighted on the mast of the flagship of
Admiral Themistocles, as tradition attests, it was received as an assurance from Pallas Athene herself that
she was fighting with and for the harassed Greeks. The
bird is displayed as large as space permits on Greek coins
of the period.

When the Romans took over Athene as Minerva her
owl came with her, but its symbolic importance quickly
faded. The Italians cared nothing for their little "strix"
—had no use for it except to eat it or make it a lure for
their bird-catching nets, and even charged it with suck-
ing the blood of children; and they had no respect at all
for the rest of its tribe. The language applied to them by

the Latin poets reveals the detestation and dread with which owls were held among the Romans. Derogatory references abound in books of the classical era, and similar sentiments might be quoted from authors down into medieval times. Even the elder Pliny, called a naturalist, but really hardly more than a too credulous compiler, condemns the tribe in very harsh words— especially the big-horned species; yet he only reflected the general belief that they were messengers of death, whence everybody trembled if one was seen in the town or alighted on any housetop. One luckless owl that made a flying trip to the Capitol was caught and burnt, and its ashes were cast into the Tiber. Twice Rome underwent ceremonial purification on this account, whence Butler's jibe in *Hudibras*:

> The Roman senate, when within
> The city walls an owl was seen,
> Did cause their clergy with lustrations
> (Our synod calls humiliations)
> The round-faced prodigy t' avert
> From doing town and country hurt.

The deaths of several Roman emperors, among them Valentinian and Commodus Antoninus, were presaged by owls alighting on their residences, and it is recorded that before the death of the great Augustus an owl sang on the Curia.

In central India the owl is now generally regarded as a bird of ill omen. "If one happens to perch on the house of a native, it is a sign that one of his household will die, or some other misfortune befall him within a year. This can only be averted by giving the house or its value in money to the Brahmins, or making extraordinary peace-offering to the gods." It is easy to calculate the origin of that particular form of superstition. In southern India, according to Thurston (quoted by Lauffer), the same dread prevails; and there the natives interpret the bird's cries by their number, much as they did those of crows. "One such screech forebodes death; two screeches, success in any approaching undertaking; three, the addition by marriage of a girl to the family; four, a disturbance; five, that the hearer will travel. Six screeches foretell the coming of guests; seven, mental distress; eight, sudden death; and nine signify favorable results. The number nine plays a great rôle in systems of divination."

In view of this Oriental and Greco-Latin history, which spread with the imperial civilization into all western Europe, and in view of the bad associations of these birds in the Old Testament, where they are pronounced "unclean," and relegated to the desert as companions of a dreadful company (*Isaiah,* xxxiv, 11), it was natural that owls should be regarded with almost insane fear and aversion in the Middle Ages, as the record shows they were. In Sweden even yet, the owl is considered a bird of sorcery, and great caution is necessary in speaking of any of them to avoid being ensnared; moreover it is dangerous to kill one, as its associates might avenge its death. Nuttall,[79] the English-American ornithologist, notes that he often heard the following couplet when he was a child in the old country:

Oh!—o-o-o—o-o !
I was once a king's daughter, and sat on my father's knee,
But now I'm a poor hoolet, and hide in a hollow tree.

This is explained in the northern counties of England by a legend that Pharaoh's daughter was transformed

into an owl, and when children hear at night the screams
of one of these nocturnal hunters they are told the story
of its strange origin—but why *Pharaoh's* daughter?
Then there is that cryptic "little ode" quoted from the
memory of his childhood by Charles Waterton [78] in reference to the barn-owl, and explained elsewhere in this
book, which runs thus:

> Once I was a monarch's daughter, and sat on a lady's knee,
> But now I'm a nightly rover, banished to the ivy-tree,
> Crying hoo, hoo, hoo, hoo, hoo, hoo, hoo, hoo, hoo, hoo,
>   for my feet are cold
> Pity me, for here you see me, persecuted, poor and old.

If the delvers into Indo-European mythology are
right, the dread of owls existed long before the Romans
colonized among Gauls and Britons, and were in turn
overrun by Teutonic hordes. It exists among the wildest savages in every part of the world where owls prowl
with ghostly silence and stealth and hoot in the darkness,
startling men's nerves, and it survives in all peasantries.
In that delightful Sicilian book by Mrs. John L.
Heaton,[80] we have a narrative of a journey after dark
with some village-women. "A screech-owl [*cuca*]
hooted. Gra Vainia crossed herself, and Donna Ciccia
muttered: 'Beautiful Mother of the Rock, deliver us!'
Donna Catina touched something [a gold cross] in the
bosom of her dress." On another occasion: "The silence
that fell again was broken by the hoot of the cuca. 'Some
one must die,' shuddered Donna Catina."

Owls have always been regarded as the familiars of
witches, sometimes bearing them through the night on
noiseless wings to some unholy tryst, sometimes con-
tributing materials to their malignant, magic-brewing
recipes. It was by meddling in such matters that the

hero of that fine old romance, *The Golden Ass* of
Apuleius, fell into his ridiculous and painful predicament.

British poets, and especially the dramatists from
Chatterton down, have taken advantage of the black repute of owls to enhance any scene of horror they want to
depict, Ben Jonson's *Masque of Queens* furnished excellent examples; and my friend J. E. Harting,[42] of
London, has gathered into his admirable *Ornithology of
Shakespeare* many owl-extracts from the great master's
play. "The owlet's wing," Mr. Harting finds, "was an
ingredient in the cauldron wherein the witches prepared
their 'charm of powerful trouble' (*Macbeth,* iv, 1);
and with the character assigned to it by the ancients,
Shakespeare, no doubt, felt that the introduction of an
owl in a dreadful scene of tragedy would help to make
the scene come home more forcibly to the people who
had from early times associated its presence with melancholy, misfortune and death. . . . Its doleful cry pierces
the ear of Lady Macbeth while the murder is being done:

> Hark! Peace!
> It was the owl that shrieked, the fatal bellman
> Which gives stern'st good-night.

"And when the murderer rushes in immediately afterwards, exclaiming 'I have done the deed. Did thou not
hear a noise?' she replies 'I have heard the owl scream.'
And later on: 'The obscure bird clamored the live-long
night!' . . . Should an owl appear at a birth, it is said
to forebode ill luck to the infant. King Henry VI, ad-
dressing Gloster, says: 'The owl shrieked at thy birth,
an evil sign'; while upon another occasion its presence
was supposed to predict a death or at least some dire mis-
hap. . . . When Richard III is irritated by the ill news

showered thick upon him, he interrupts the third messenger with 'Out on ye, Owls! Nothing but songs of
death.'"

It is not surprising on turning to the medieval phar-
macopœia, where there was quite as much magic as
medicine, that the owl was of great potency in prescrip-
tions. "Thus the feet of the bubo, burnt with hard
plumbago, was held to be a help against serpents. If the
heart of the bird was placed on the left breast of a sleeping beauty, it made her tell all her secrets: but the
warrior who carried it was strengthened in battle." A
modern relic of this bit of superstitious therapeutics was
found by me in *The Long Hidden Friend*, a little book
printed at Carlisle, Pennsylvania, in 1863, which was a
crude translation by George Homan of a German book
published at Reading, Penn., in 1819. It consists of a
long series of remedies and magic arts to be followed,
and which were actually in use in that region in cases of
disease. Some of them introduced birds, one of which
is reminiscent of the "sleeping beauty" mentioned a
moment ago, and reads thus: "If you lay the heart and
right foot of a barn-owl on one who is asleep, he will
answer whatever you ask him, and tell what he has done."
This should be known to our chiefs of police, whose de-
tectives appear to be wasting much time in applying the
extractive process called the Third Degree.

The owl tribe, among the most innocent and service-
able, in its relation to mankind, of avian groups, has been
as outrageously slandered south of the Mediterranean as
north of it. "The inhabitants of Tangier," as Colonel Irby
tells us [81] in his book on the ornithology of Gibraltar, consider the barn-owls, numerous there, "the clairvoyant
friends of the Devil."

The Jews believe that their cry causes the death of
young children; so, in order to prevent this, they pour
a vessel of water out into the courtyard every time they
hear the cry of one of these owls, the idea being that
thus they will distract the bird's attention, and the
infant will escape the intended malice. The Arabs believe these owls can cause all kinds of evil to old as
well as young, but they content themselves with cursing
the bird whenever it is seen or heard. The Mohammedans say: "When these birds cry they are only cursing in their own language; but their malediction is harm-
less unless they know the name of the individual to
whom they wish evil, or unless they have the malignity
to point out that person when passing him. As the Devil
sleeps but little when there is evil work to be done, he
would infallibly execute the commands of his favorite,
if one did not, by cursing him, thus guard against the
power of that enemy."

It is a pleasure to have this long record of misde-
meanors and diabolism relieved by at least one good deed
in history. Having read in Watters's [57] curious little
volume that the Tartars attribute to the barn-owl the
saving of the life of their great commander Genghis
Khan, I searched far and wide for the particulars of what
seemed likely to be an entertaining incident, and at last
I came upon the facts in the eleventh volume of *Purchase
His Pilgrims*. It appears that Changius Can, as the old
historian spells it, had his horse shot under him in a
certain fight that was going against him, and he ran and
hid in a thicket of shrubs—which is a novel view of the
"Tartar Terror." "Whither, when the enemies were
returned, with purpose to spoil the dead Carkass, and to
seek out such as were hidden, it happened that an Owle

came and sate upon those little trees or shrubs which he had chose for his court, which when they had perceived they sought no further in that place, supposing that the said bird would not have sat there if any man had been hidden underneath."

A very similar legend in China accounts for the use of peacock plumes as insignia of rank and is related as follows by Katherine M. Ball [68]: In the Chin dynasty a defeated general took refuge in a forest where there were many peacocks. When the pursuing forces arrived, and found the fowl so quiet and undisturbed, they concluded that no one could possibly have come that way, and forthwith abandoned the search. The general—who later became the ancestor of five kings—was thus able to escape, and so grateful was he that later, when he came into power, he instituted the custom of conferring a peacock feather as an honor for the achievement of bravery in battle.

Japan has a similar mythical legend.

Frenchmen call the common brown owl of Europe *chouette;* and when in 1793 disgruntled smugglers and Royalist soldiers were carrying on guerrilla warfare in Brittany and Poitu against the new order of things, they came to be called Chouans, "owls," from the signal-cries they made to one another in their nocturnal forays as appears so often in Balzac's novel *The Chouans.*

Not much of this spookish and legendary lore seems to have been imported into the United States, or else it has disappeared, except that which still lingers among the superstitious negroes of the South. A writer in one of the early issues of *The Cosmopolitan* (magazine) related that to the black folks of the Cotton Belt forty years or so ago the quavering "song" of our small mottled screech-owl spoke of coming death; but the birds were considered sensitive to countercharms put upon them from within the house over which they crooned their tremulous monologue. "Jest jam de shevel inter de fire, en time hit git red-hot dee 'll hesh dere shiverin'!" If you don't like that, sprinkle salt on the blaze, or turn a pair of shoes up on the floor with the soles against the wall. "Perhaps this faint semblance to a laid-out corpse will pacify the hungry spirit; the charm certainly, according to negro belief, will silence its harsh-voiced emissary."

The darkies warn you that you must turn back on any journey you are making if a screech-owl cries above you. An old "hoot-owl," however, may foretell either good or bad fortune according as its three hoots are given on the right or left hand. This is an unfailing sign, and is especially heeded in 'coon or 'possum hunting, at night, when three hoots from the left will send any hunter home hopeless.

All these indications and charms bear the familiar marks of the Old World fears and formulas, but it is surprising to meet them on the fields of Dixie-land.

Owls were too well understood by our native redmen to be regarded with much superstition, and the smaller ones were well liked. Prince Maximilian mentions in his *Travels* (about 1836) that owls were kept in the lodges of the Mandans and Minnitarees, who lived in permanent villages in the upper Missouri Valley, and were regarded as "soothsayers," but I think they were no more than pets, as they are now in Zuñi houses. Yet in the American Museum of Natural History in New York is a stuffed owl mounted on a stick, labeled as an object "worshipped" by the sorcerers among the Menominee Indians (eastern Wisconsin), "who believe they can assume the shape of an owl, and can in this disguise attack and kill their enemies"—that is, they try to make others believe so. The owl is chosen for their disguise, of course, because it typifies the sly, unseen method of attack in darkness with which they sought to terrify the people.

Mr. Stuart Culin tells me that in Zuñi owls, of which four kinds are recognized by names, are not considered sacred, and are killed for their feathers, which are used on ceremonial masks, and, once a year, to decorate long prayer-sticks. The people, he says, think that a certain big gray owl lives in a house like a man, and if any Indian goes to its house and the owl looks at him he will surely die. When the headmen go out at night for some ceremony, and this owl is heard, it is a sign that rain will come very soon. This large owl and the small burrowing-owl are kept in houses as pets. Children are afraid of them, and they are utilized .by parents to make the youngsters behave themselves.

The Ashochimi, a mountain tribe of Californian Indians now extinct, as described by Powers, [19] feared certain hawks and owls, regarding them as malignant spirits which they must conciliate by offerings, and by wearing mantles of feathers, thus:

When a great white owl alights near a village in the evening, and hoots loudly, the headman at once assembles all his warriors in council to determine whether Mr Strix demands a life or only money. . . . If they incline to believe that he demands a life, someone in the village is doomed and will speedily die. But they generally vote that he can be placated by an offering, and immediately set out a quantity of shell-money and pinole, whereupon the valorous trenchermen fall to eat the pinole themselves, and in the morning the headman decorates himself with owl-feathers, carries out the shell-money with solemn formality and flings it into the air under the tree where the owl perched.

A somewhat more spiritual view was taken by the Pimas of old times in the southwestern deserts. Their ideas of the destiny of the human soul varied, but one theory was that at death the soul passed into the body of an owl. "Should an owl happen to be hooting at the time of a death, it was believed that it was waiting for the soul. . . . Owl-feathers were always given to a dying person. They were kept in a long, rectangular box or basket of maguey leaf. If the family had no owl-feathers at hand they sent to the medicine-man who always kept them. If possible, the feathers were taken from a living bird when collected; the owl might then be set free or killed." [83]

CHAPTER X

A FLOCK OF FABULOUS FOWLS

WE are pretty sure to hear of the phenix every time a tailor or soap-maker announces that he will rebuild his shop after it has been burned; and its picture is a favorite with the advertising department of fire-insurance companies. The world first learned of this remarkable fowl when Herodotus brought back to Greece his wonder-tales from Egypt, some 400 years before Cleopatra made so much trouble by mixing love and politics. It will be well to quote in full the account by the great Greek traveller as it is found in the translation by Laurent:

There is another sacred bird, called the "phenix," which I myself never saw except in a picture, for it seldom makes its appearance among the Egyptians—only every five-hundred years, according to the people of Heliopolis. They state that he comes on the death of his sire. If at all like his picture, this bird may be thus described in size and shape. Some of his feathers are of the color of gold; others are red. In outline he is exceedingly similar to the eagle, and in size also. This bird is said to display an ingenuity which to me does not appear credible: he is represented as coming out of Arabia, and bringing with him his father to the temple of the Sun, embalmed in myrrh, and there burying him. The manner in which this is done is as follows: In the first place he sticks together an egg of myrrh, as much as he can carry, and then tries if he can bear the burden. This experiment achieved, he accordingly scoops out the egg sufficiently to deposit his sire within. He next fills with fresh myrrh the opening in the egg by which the body was inclosed; thus the whole mass contain-

ing the carcase is still of the same weight. Having thus completed the embalming, he transports him into Egypt and to the
temple of the Sun. (*Euterpe,* Book II.)

Herodotus seems to have been most interested in the
odorous embalming, quaintly referred to in a 17th-
century song—

> Have you e'r smelt what Chymick Skill
> From Rose or Amber doth distill?
> Have you been near that Sacrifice
> The Phoenix makes before she dies?

And it will be noticed that this observant reporter says
nothing of the quality that has given the bird its present
popularity as a type of recovery from disaster—its ability
to "rise from its ashes," which, indeed, appears to have
been a later conception.

Greeks of that day probably accepted this story from
Herodotus without much demur or criticism, for they
had their own traditions of wonderful birds—the
Stymphalids, for example. These were gigantic and
terrible fowls that lived along the river Stymphalus, in
northern Arcadia—a region of savage mountains that
the Athenians knew little about. They were believed to
be man-eating monsters with claws, wings, and beaks of
brass, and feathers which they shot out like arrows.
"Heracles scared them with a brazen rattle, and succeeded
in killing part and in driving away the rest, which settled
on the island of Artias in the Black Sea, to be frightened
away after a hard fight by the Argonauts." So Seyfert
summarizes their history; and an illustration on an antique vase in the Metropolitan Museum of Art shows a
flock of them looking much like pelicans.

Pausanias visited the curious River Stymphalus and

found it rising in a spring, flowing into a marsh, and then disappearing underground—a good setting for strange happenings, and he refers to the legend in his usual bantering way, thus:

"There is a tradition that some man-eating birds lived on its banks, whom Hercules is said to have killed with his arrows. . . . The desert of Arabia has among other monsters some birds called Stymphalides, who are as savage to men as lions or leopards. They attack those who come to capture them, and wound them with their beaks and kill them. They pierce through coats of mail that men wear, and if they put on thick robes of mat the beaks of these birds penetrate them too. . . . Their size is about that of cranes and they are like storks, but their beaks are stronger and not crooked like those of storks. If there have been in all time these stymphalides like hawks and eagles, then they are probably of Arabian origin."

The Greeks knew also of half-human Harpies, of web-footed Sirens, of the Birds of Seleucia, and of various other ornithological monstrosities, so that the tale of an Egyptian one was easily acceptable to their minds. The ugliest of the ugly flock were the Harpies, bird-women, on whom the ancients expended the direst pigments of their imagination, and whom Dante makes inhabitants of the gnarled and gloomy groves wherein suicides are condemned to suffer in the nether world—

There do the hideous Harpies make their nests
Who chased the Trojans from the Strophades
With sad announcement of impending doom;
Broad wings have they, and necks and faces human,
And feet with claws, and their great bellies fledged
They make lament upon the wondrous trees.

The Romans liked Herodotus and his story as well as they pleased the Greeks, and Pliny heard or invented

additional particulars.   He insists that only one phenix
exists at a time, clothed in gorgeous feathers and carrying
a plumed head; and at the close of its long life it builds
a nest of frankincense and cassia, on which it dies.
From the corpse, as Pliny asserts, is generated a worm
that develops into another phenix.   This young phenix,
when it has grown large enough, makes it its first duty to
lay its father's body on the altar in Heliopolis; and
Tacitus adds that its body is burned there.   The implication in most accounts is that the bird is male (the
Egyptians are said to have believed all vultures female),
and doubtless the whole conception is a primitive phase
of the nature-worship out of which developed the more
formal Osiris-legend.

But the picture has many variants.   One is that the
phenix subsists on air for 500 years, at the end of which,
lading its wings with perfumed gums gathered on Mt.
Lebanon (!) it flies to Heliopolis and is burned—*itself*
now, not its parent—into fragrant ashes on the altar of
the Sun temple.   On the next morning appears a young
phenix already feathered, and on the third day, its pinions
fully grown, it salutes the priest and flies away.   Here
we come to the best remembered feature of the mystery,
caught and kept alive for us by the poets, such as John
Lyly,[49] who in 1591 reminded the world that—

> There is a bird that builds its neast with spice,
>   And built, the Sun to ashes doth her burne,
> Out of whose sinders doth another rise,
>   And she by scorching beames to dust doth turne.

De Kay [18] discourses on these notions in his *Bird Gods:*

"In the oldest tombs, discovered lately on the upper Nile by
Jacques de Morgan and others, the phenix is seen rising from

a bed of flames, which may well mean the funeral pyre of the defunct. The inscriptions in question are so early that they belong to a period when the ceremonial of the mummy had not become universal in Egypt, and the conquerors of Egypt, prob- ably a swarm of metal-using foreigners from the valley of the Euphrates, who crossed from Arabia and the Red Sea, were still burning the bodies of their chiefs and kings. The phenix of these inscriptions may indicate the soul of the departed rising from its earthly dross as the soul of Herakles, according to the much later legend in its Greek form, rose from his funeral pyre to join the gods of Olympus."

Now, whether or not the priests of Heliopolis en- couraged their worshippers to believe that such a creature really existed, they themselves knew well that it was a mere symbol of the sun; and it is easy to identify it with the bird "bennu" spoken of in the Book of the Dead and other Egyptian sacred texts, which unquestionably was a picturesque representative of the sun, rising, pursuing its course, and at regular intervals expiring in the fires of sunset, then renewing itself on the morrow in the flames of sunrise over Arabia. Plentiful evidence that this was perfectly understood in Greece and Italy of the classic age may be read in the works of their essayists and poets. Claudian (365-408), wrote, and Tickell, a British poet, translated into verse, a long poem on the phenix. Petrarch carried their wisdom onward when he declared there could be only one phenix at a time because there was only one sun.

When the Arabs succeeded the Romans in the Nile Provinces they picked up from the people remnants of the legend, and confused it with their own ancient belief in a creature that resisted burning, by whose existence they accounted for the incombustible property of asbestos, a mineral known to them, but the origin of which was a mystery. It came from the Orient, and some said it was

a vegetable product, others the hair of a rat-like animal:
the western Arabs, however, mostly believed it to be the
plumage of a bird, so that naturally they identified it with
the fire-loving phenix. Arabian authors of the 10th century and onward describe this bird, under the Greek name
"salamandra," as dwelling in India, where it lays its eggs
and produces young in fire. Sashes, they say, are made
of its feathers, and when one of them becomes soiled it
is thrown on a fire, and comes out whole, but clean.

This is an excellent example of the mingling of fact
and fancy by which a student of these old matters is constantly perplexed. It is probable that small woven
articles had long been known to the Arabs and Moors
as Eastern curiosities, for the people of southern China
since very ancient times had been collecting and preparing
fibrous asbestos, and weaving it into fire-proof cloth.
Such fabrics had, no doubt, a rough, fuzzy surface, not
unlike fur or the down of birds, and might easily be supposed to be the latter. Hence the assertion that asbestos
was the skin of a bird indestructible by fire, the identifica-
tion of the phenix with the salamandra (as a bird—it had
other legendary forms), and the trade-name "samand"
given to asbestos cloth when the Arabs themselves began
to manufacture and sell it. So our proverbial idea of the
salamander goes back to a remote antiquity; but how it
came to be represented among us as a newt instead of a
bird belongs to another book.

Meanwhile on the northern shore of the Mediterranean,
where the legend of the phenix was popular, it had been
introduced into Christianity as a symbol, as we know
from memorial sculpture, and from the writings of St.
Clement, who was the second pope after Peter. Its special
meaning was immortality, which in that period meant the

physical resurrection of the dead; and the peacock came
to be used in the same sense, as representing, if not
virtually merged with, the phenix. The image in men's
minds at that time appears to have been that of an eagle,
a bird closely identified with the sun, clothed in the
plumage of the peacock, another sun-bird (as representative of the gorgeous clouds at sunset) ; and the very name
confirms these solar associations, for our "phenix" is the
Greek word *phoinix,* crimson red. How large a place the
peacock in this aspect fills in the art and mythology of
China and Japan appears in Chapter VII.

Hulme informs us that Philippe de Thaum writes in
his *Bestiary* of the mystic bird: "Know this is its lot; it
comes to death of its own will, and from death it comes
to life: hear what it signifies. Phoenix signifies Jesus,
Son of Mary, that he had power to die of his own will,
and from death come to life. Phoenix signifies that to
save his people he chose to suffer upon the cross." "God
knew men's unbelief," St. Cyril laments, "and therefore
provided this bird as evidence of the Resurrection." St.
Ambrose also declares that "the bird of Arabia teaches
us, by its example, to believe in the Resurrection." Passages of like tenor might be quoted from Tertullian and
other expositors of the early Christian church, all showing the most unsuspicious faith in the real existence of
such a bird.

The symbolic connection of this fabulous creature with
the idea of immortality may have been an inheritance
from Jewish traditions. According to the Talmud Eve,
after eating the terrible fruit in the Garden of Eden,
tried to force it, and its consequences, on all the animals,
but the bird "chol" (the phenix) would not eat, but flew
away from temptation, and thus preserved its original

gift of perpetual life. "And now the phenix . . . lives a
thousand years, then shrivels up till it is the size of an
egg, and then from himself emerges beautiful again."
In the Middle Ages this deathless bird was supposed to
inhabit the sacred garden of the Earthly Paradise.

Peacocks carved on early Christian sarcophagi are
perched on a palm tree (the conventional sign of martyrdom in primitive Christian iconography), and hence elo-
quent of that rapturous belief in immortality characteristic of the catacombs, as Mrs. Jenner expresses it. Representations of the bird rising from a flaming nest and
ascending toward the sun are less common, but do occur
in medieval heraldry, by which pictorial path, it is probable, the notion has come down to our own day and become the cognizance of one of the oldest American in-
surance companies.

The association with the palm mentioned above recalls another line of legendry, for some etymologists say
that the name "phenix" should be so written (not
phoenix), and that it is the older name of the date-palm.
This tree was regarded in ancient Egypt as the emblem
of triumph, whence, perhaps, our modern symbolic use
of its fronds; and Pliny was informed that "in Arabia
the phenix nested only on a palm," and that "the said
bird died with the tree and revived of itself as the tree
sprang again."

Now, Arabic authors of the Middle Ages had much
to say of a mythical bird, "anka," that lived 1700 years;
and they explained that when a young anka grows up if it
be a female the old female burns herself, and if it be a male
the old male does so. This is very phenix-like, but the anka
is distinguished by huge size, the Arabic writer Kazweenee,
as quoted by Payne,[87] describing the anka as the greatest

of birds. "It carries off the elephant," he says, "as the
cat carries off the mouse"; and he relates that in consequence of its kidnapping a bride God, at the prayer of the
prophet Handhallah, "banished it to an island in the cir-
cumambient ocean unvisited by men under the equinoctial
line."

I find in Miss Costello's *Rose Garden of Persia* [88] some
interesting notes quoted from M. Garcin de Tassy, relative to the anka, which, De Tassy says, has become a
proverbial symbol in Persia for something spoken of
but not seen—and not likely to be! Here he seems to be
using the Arabic name for the bird the Persians call
"simurgh," the signification of which, as Professor
A. V. W. Jackson tells me, is "the mythical," and which
is derived from the avestan word for "eagle"—another
link in our chain. De Tassy explains:

It [the anka] is known only by name, and is so called from
having a white line round the neck like a collar; some say because of the length of the neck. . . . It is said that the inhabitants of the city of Res. . . . had in their country a mountain
called Demaj, a mile high. There came a very large bird with
a very long neck, of beautiful and divers colors. This bird was
accustomed to pounce on all the birds of that mountain, and
eat them up. One day he was hungry and birds were scarce,
so he pounced on a child and carried it off. He is called anka-
mogreb because he carries off the prey he seizes. . . . Soon
after this he was struck by a thunderbolt.

Mohammed is reported to have said that at the time of
Moses God created a female bird called anka; it had eight
wings like the seraphs, and bore the figure of a man. God gave
it a portion of every thing, and afterwards created it a male.
Then God made a revelation to Moses that he had created two
extraordinary birds, and had assigned for their nourishment
the wild beasts around Jerusalem. But the species multiplied,
and when Moses was dead they went to the land of Nejd and
Hijaz, and never ceased to devour the wild beasts and to carry
off children till the time when Khaled, son of Senan Abasi,

was Prophet, between the time of Christ and Mohammed. It was then that these birds were complained of. Khaled invoked God, and God did not permit them to multiply, and their race became extinct.

This characteristic Bedouin camp-fire novelette reminds us at once of the famous roc, or "rukh," to adopt the more correct spelling, with which we are familiar from the story in the *Arabian Nights* of Sinbad the Sailor. Let me quote it succinctly from Payne's edition.[87] Sinbad had sailed on a commercial venture from his home in Basra, a port on the Persian Gulf, and the ship had stopped at a very pleasant island, situation unrecorded. Sinbad went ashore with others, wandered in the lovely woods, fell asleep, and awoke to find the ship gone and himself the only person on the island. As he was exploring the place rather timidly he came to a great shining dome, but could see no doorway. "As I stood," he relates, "casting about how to gain an entrance, the sun was suddenly hidden from me and the air became dark. . . ."

So I marvelled at this, and lifting my head looked steadfastly at the sun, when I saw that what I had taken for a cloud was none other than an enormous bird whose outspread wings, as it flew through the air, obscured the sun and veiled it from the island. At this sight my wonder redoubled, and I bethought me of a story I had heard aforetime of pilgrims and travellers, how in certain islands dwells a huge bird, called the roc, which feeds its young on elephants, and was assured that the dome aforesaid was none other than one of its eggs. As I looked . . . the bird alighted on the egg and brooded over it, with its wings covering it and its legs spread out behind it on the ground, and in this posture it fell asleep, glory be to Him who sleepeth not!

When I saw this I arose, and unwinding the linen of my turban twisted it into a rope with which I girt my middle, and bound myself fast to his feet.

Sinbad's purpose was to get himself carried away to some better place, but when, next morning, the roc did bear him aloft and afar, and finally alighted, the sailor found himself in a horrid desert. After many further adventures and voyages Sinbad revisits his island yet does not recognize it until the men with whom he is strolling bade him look at a great dome. Not knowing what it was they broke it open with stones, "whereupon much water ran out of it, and the young roc appeared within; so they pulled it forth of the shell and killed it, and took of it great store of meat." Dreadful misfortune followed this inconsiderate act.

This was a well-known Arabic wonder-tale. The author of one of their popular old books of "marvels," several of which exist, tells almost exactly Sinbad's story as happening to himself, and at least two other Arabic works are said to contain the tale with picturesque variations. In later times the home of the monster was placed in Madagascar. Marco Polo, the adventurous Italian, who in the 13th century wandered overland to China, and whose *Travels*[89] are a fine mixture of fact and fancy, had a fair idea of where Madagascar was, and recorded much that he was told about it—mostly erroneous. He relates that the people of that island report "That at a certain season of the year . . . the rukh makes its appearance from the southern region. . . . Persons who have seen this bird assert that when the wings are spread they measure sixteen paces in extent." Marco says that he heard that the agents of the Grand Khan took to him a feather ninety spans long. It is explained in Yule's edition of Polo's *Travels* that the supposed roc's feather was one of the gigantic fronds of the raphia palm "very like a quill in form."

Such wonder-tales have a truly phenixlike quality of indestructibility. As late as the time of Charles I of England there lived in Lambeth, on the Surrey side of London, John Tradescant, renowned as traveller and florist, who accumulated an extensive "physic-garden" and museum of antiquities and curiosities. He was a man of science, but to satisfy the popular taste of the time, as Pennant explains, his museum contained a feather alleged to be of the dragon, and another of the griffin. "You might have found here two feathers of the tail of the *phoenix,* and the claw of the *rukh,* a bird capable to *trusse* an elephant." This collection after the death of Tradescant's son in 1622, became the property of Elias Ashmole, and it was the nucleus of the Ashmolean Museum founded at Oxford in 1682.

But phenix, rukh, anka, simurgh, garuda, feng-huang and others that have not been mentioned, such as Yel, the mythical raven of our Northwest, and those of Malaya described by Skeat,[7] are all, apparently, members of the brood hatched ages ago in that same sunrise nest and still flying amid rosy clouds of prehistoric fable.

The first glimpse of them is on the seals and tablets recovered from Mesopotamian ruin-mounds. In the mystic antiquity of the Summerian kingdom of Ur and its capital-city Lagash, a gigantic eagle, "the divine bird Imgig" was the royal cognizance. In those days, as Dr. Ward[28] discloses from his study of the oldest Babylonian cylinders, people told one another tales of monstrous and fantastic birds of prey that could fly away with an antelope in each talon, and which fought, usually victoriously, against huge winged and feathered dragons with bodies like those of crocodiles, and sometimes with human heads.

Such representations of demons were the prototypes of the grotesque combinations of animal features, and of men and animals, more familiar to us in the Egyptian Sphinx, the classic centaurs, and medieval angels and devils.

When the elders in Babylon expounded the reason for faith in these antagonistic supernatural creatures, they explained that the "divine" eagle symbolized beneficence and protective power in the universe, while the feathered monsters stood for the baffling forces of malignancy and harm. In this philosophy, probably, is the underlying relationship that connects all this Oriental flock of fabulous fowls—visionary flight-beings in varying forms and phases that seek to portray the powers of the air, mysterious, uncontrollable, overwhelming, capable of all the mind of primitive man could conceive or his gods perform. All of them became endowed in time with the luxuriant colorings of Eastern poetry and fiction, and appear now heroic and picturesque, as one expects of everything in the dreamy Orient of tradition.

In the cold and stormy North, however, where the sun is a source of comfort rather than of terror, and movements of the atmosphere are more often feared than blessed, the similar conception of a gigantic skybird is far more definite. When the native of the Russian plains, struggling homeward against driving snow, hears the shrilling and howling of the tempest he knows Vikhar, the Wind-Demon, is abroad. Norsemen represent him as Hraesvelg, the North Wind, an eagle: he does not "ride on the wings of the wind," he *is* the wind, and the blast from the arctic sea that beats upon your face is the air set in motion by the wings of this colossal, invisible

bird flying southward. That it is big enough to stir the
atmosphere into a veritable hurricane is plain:

> From the East came flying hither,
> From the East a monstrous eagle,
> One wing touched the vault of heaven,
> While the other swept the ocean;
> With his tail upon the waters,
> Reached his beak beyond the cloudlets.

And such an eagle as this one, described as a reality in
the *Kalevala,* the legendary epic of the Finns, possessing
beak and talons of copper, once seized and bore away a
maiden to its eyrie, thus showing itself true to the "form"
of the East whence it came.

Most of our North American Indians typified the
winds, especially those from the north, as birds, and many
tribes identified the storm-bringing ones with their
thunder-birds, which was very natural. The Algonkins
believed that certain birds produced the phenomena of
wind and created waterspouts, and that the clouds were
the spreading and agitation of their gigantic wings. The
Navahos thought that a great white swan sat at each of the
four points of the compass and conjured up the blasts
that came therefrom, while the Dakotas believed that in
the west is the residence of the Wakinyjan, "the Flyers,"
that is, the breezes that develop into occasional storms.

It was in the Orient, however, where, by the way,
both simurgh and garuda serve as storm-bringers in
several myths, that the conception of gigantic bird-beings
was expanded and elaborated with the picturesque details
that have been suggested in an earlier paragraph.

A very old Persian tale, with many fanciful embroider-
ings, runs as follows: There are, or were, two trees—

one the Tree of Life, and the other the Tree Opposed to
All Harm, the tree that bears the seeds of all useful
things; which is like the two trees in the Garden of
Eden, over in Babylon. In the latter tree sits and nests
the chief of all the mythic birds, the simurgh (called in the
Avesta "saena-meregha"), which is said to suckle its
young, and to be three natures "like a bat." "Whenever
he arises aloft a thousand twigs will shoot out from that
tree, and when he alights he breaks off the thousand twigs
and bites the seeds from them. And the bird cinamros
[second only to the simurgh] alights likewise in that
vicinity; and his work is this, that he collects those seeds
that are bitten from the tree of many seeds, which is
opposed to harm, and he scatters them where Tishtar
[angel that provides rain] seizes the water [from the
demons of drought] ; so that, while Tishtar shall seize the
water, together with those seeds of all kinds, he shall
rain them on the world with the rain." Such is the language of the sacred books.[26]

The simurgh figures in Firdausi's [93] legendary epic as
the foster-parent of Zal, father of Rustam, the national
hero of Persia. When Rudabah's flank was opened to
bring forth Rustam her wound was healed by rubbing it
with a simurgh's feather. Rustam himself, once wounded
unto death, was cured in the same manner, and other
cases are recorded in great variety. Firdausi explains
that the simurgh had its nest on Mt. Elburz, on a peak
that touched the sky in a place no man had ever seen;
and that it was to that eyrie that it carried the princely
baby Zal, whence it was recovered by its parents. In
the ancient Avestan ritual it is stated of the vulture
varengana: "If a man holds a bone of that strong bird
. . . or a feather, no one can smite or turn to flight that

fortunate man. The feather of that bird brings him help . . . maintains him in his glory." According to De Kay [18] the simurgh was a "god-like bird that discussed predestination with Solomon, as the eagle of Givernberg held dialogues with King Arthur. . . . The simurgh was a prophet."

But of all the fabulous birds that infest ancient Persian mythology none is held so important as the falcon-like "karshipta," which brought the sacred law into the Paradise of Jamshid. "Regarding the karshipta they say that it knew how to speak words, and brought the religion to the enclosure which Yim made, and circulated it: there they utter the Avesta in the language of birds."

We read also of a gigantic bird in Iran, the "kamar," "which overshadowed the earth and kept off the rain till the rivers dried up."

In the Hindu mythology Vishnu is the sun-god, while Indra represents the lightning and storm, and the two are in general opposites, rivals, enemies. Vishnu rides on an eagle of supernatural size and power called garuda. In the Pahlavi translation of the stories the simurgh takes the place of the eagle, for their characters as well as their names are interchangeable. Garuda was born from an egg laid by Vinata, herself the daughter of a hawk and the mother of the two immense vultures that in Persian myths guard the gates of hell, and elsewhere figure boldly in Oriental fables; it is a mortal enemy, now of the serpent and now of the elephant, and now of the tortoise— all three connected with Indra. This bird carries into the air an elephant and a tortoise in order to devour them, and in one of the various accounts leaves them on a mountain-top as did the simurgh and the rukh their iniquitous "liftings."

Garuda also appears in Japanese legendary art as gario, or binga, or bingacho, or karobinga, half woman, half bird, a sort of winged and feathered angel with a tail like a phenix and legs like a crane. This reminds us of the harpies of Greece. The Malays recognize the image, and when a cloud obscures the sun Perak men will say: "Gerda is spreading his wings to dry."

The Chinese, and after them the Japanese, had a phenix-like bird in their mythical aviary, which persists in the faith of the more simple-minded of their peoples, and as a fruitful motive in the decorative art of each. It was one of the four supernatural creatures that in ancient Chinese philosophy symbolized the four quarters of the heavens. The Taoists, whose religious ideas are older than Confucianism and prevailed especially among the humble and unlearned, called it the Scarlet Bird, and associated it with the element Fire, and with their mystic number 7. Archaic pictures show a crested bird with long tail-feathers—a figure that might well be meant for a peacock. The creature itself is said not to have been seen by mortal eyes since the time of Confucius, but it has by no means been forgotten, for it is the fung-whang, or feng-huang (which is the names of the male and the female of the species conjoined); and it lives even now on embroidered screens and painted vases, or proudly distinguishes royal robes, from the Thibetan mountains to the Yellow Sea.

A recent writer on Eastern art [68] describes the proper fung as a gorgeously colored bird with a long tail. Its feathers are red, azure, yellow, white, and black, the five colors belonging to the five principal virtues; and the Chinese ideograms for uprightness, humanity, virtue, honesty, and sincerity, are impressed on various parts of

its body. Its cries are symbolic, its appearance precedes
the advent of virtuous rulers. As in the other cases
this bird carries something away—this time an eminent
philosopher, Baik-fu, was translated. In Japan the
peasantry, at least, still hold to the reality of the same
bird under the name ho-ho, and artists and symbolists
have beautifully utilized the conception. [90] The belief
is that the sun descends to earth from time to time in the
form of the ho-ho, as a messenger of love, peace, and
goodwill, and rests on one or another of the torii. It
appears to have become a badge of imperial rank in
China before the time of the Ming dynasty, and, in
Japan it became the symbol of the empress, and in old
times, as we are told, only empresses and royal princesses
could have its likeness woven into their dress-goods.

It will be noticed that this last-considered member of
our fabulous flock, the fung-whang or ho-ho, is the
only one not of gigantic size or distorted or terrifying
aspect. This indicates to me its comparatively recent
origin, and its beneficent disposition shows that it is the
creation of men accustomed to peace under kindly skies.
It is an interesting fact that when the Mongolian felt
called upon to portray demoniac beings he exaggerated to
the extent of his ability *human* expressions of rage,
villainy and ferocity, instead of using for his purpose
animals of Titanic size, or in horrifying combinations,
as did magicians south of the great mountains.

The explanation seems not far away. The territory
that apparently always has been the home of the homo-
geneous "yellow" race is essentially a vast plain extending from the mountains of central Asia westward to the
Pacific and meridianally from southern China to the
border of Kamptchatka. It includes the spacious valleys

of China, proper, the plains and deserts of Mongolia, and the broad prairies that stretch across Manchuria, making together the widest area of fairly level and tillable land on the globe. Much of it was never forested, and from a large part of the remainder the scanty growth of woods had been cleared before written history began. The climate as a whole is temperate and equable, and rarely disturbed by startling and destructive meteorological phenomena. Furthermore, except the tigers of the jungly southeastern border, no dangerous animals are to be feared or to be idealized into mythical things of terror. Two evils of nature remain to disturb the inhabitants of this favored region—annual spring-floods, often fatally widespread; and, second, frequent earthquakes. The floods are perfectly understood in their cause as well as in their effects, and afford little material for superstition. As for the earthquakes, the people long ago found a sufficient explanation in the invention of a burrowing beast of prodigious size and strength, which they called an "earth-dragon," and whose movements as it stirs about heaves the ground beneath our feet. The wave-like character of the earth-shocks showed that the dragon must be elongated and reptile-like; and now and then a landslide or diggings disclosed long and massive bones that evidently were those of these subterranean monsters, although foreigners said they were fossil remains of Mesozoic reptiles or something else. The whole idea, in fact, is so plausible and logical, that it really belongs to scientific hypothesis rather than to mythology.

The reaction of this tranquil geographical situation and history has been to produce, or mould, a people gentle, self-contained and averse to strife. This is not particularly to their credit or their discredit. It is as natural for a race developed in the valley of the Hoang Ho to be peaceable as for one bred along the Danube or the St. Lawrence to be belligerent.

In such an unterrifying situation as his the Mongolian felt no impulse to coin the manifestations of nature, elemental or animated, into malignant demons, but rather impersonated them, if at all, as beings with kindly intentions and of beautiful form. That such impersonations are few, and that Chinese mythology furnishes a comparatively small contribution to the world's store of specimens of that primitive stage in human mentality, is, I think, another evidence of the equable physical environment in which the people of the Flowery Kingdom have been nurtured, which, while it contributed to their sanity, did little to stimulate their imaginations.

On the other hand, men and women who endured, day by day, the blistering heat and drouth of the desert; or who knew the awe-inspiring mountains, where gloomy glens alternate with cloud-veiled heights, the thunders of unseen avalanches shock the ear, and appalling fires that no man kindles rage against the snows; or who night and day must guard his or her life in the jungle against lurking perils from tooth and claw and poison-fang—such persons were aroused to mental as well as physical alertness for safety's sake, and saw in almost every circumstance of their lives visions of unearthly power. Unable in their narrow, slowly developing knowledge and meagre intellection, to comprehend much of what confronted them, yet understanding some small sources and agencies of power, what more natural than that they should picture the often tremendous exhibitions of nature's force as the product of enormously *greater* powers. Hence not only the bigness attributed to the mythical birds we have sketched but their supernatural abilities, and also—in accordance with constant experience of the general antagonism between nature and human purposes—the malignancy characterizing most of them.

For, as has been said, Garuda, Simurgh, Phenix, Fung-Whang and all the others are only visions woven out of the sunshine, the clouds and the winds, in the loom of primitive imagination. It is quite a waste of time, therefore, to try as some have done (notably Professor Newton [55]) to connect any one of them with some living or extinct reality, as, for example, the Rukh with the epiornis or any other of the big extinct ratite birds of Madagascar. Eagles and vultures and peacocks have served as suggestions for fantastic creations of a vagrant fancy, and that is all the reality they ever had. We do not know, probably never can know, the ultimate source of these stories and images, so varied yet so alike; nor whether all have spread from one source, or have in some instances arisen independently, as would seem probable in the case of those told about American aboriginal campfires; but we may be sure that their conception was in the morning of civilization (more likely far back of that) as products of the uncultured, nature-fearing, marvel-loving fancy of prehistoric mankind.

CHAPTER XI

FROM ANCIENT AUGURIES TO MODERN RAINBIRDS

THE pagans of primitive times along the shores of the Mediterranean believed in personal gods and their guidance in human affairs. With the approval of these gods, or of that departmental god or goddess having charge of the matter in mind, one's project would prosper, whereas their disapproval meant failure and very likely some punishment under divine wrath. The human difficulty was to learn the will of said gods.

Equally well settled was the doctrine that birds—which seemed to belong to the celestial spaces overhead where the gods lived and manifested their variable moods, now in sunshine and zephyr, now by storm-clouds, and rainfall —were inspired messengers of the gods, and required reverent attention. This, however, did but throw the difficulty one step further back, for how could human intelligence comprehend the messages birds were constantly bringing?

At any rate the principal and most numerous omens in the pre-Christian centuries were drawn from birds; and this kind of divination gained so much credit that other kinds were little regarded. It was based, as has been indicated, on the theory that these creatures, by their actions, wittingly or unwittingly, conveyed the will of the gods. This super-avian attribute was by no means confined to the prominent raven and crow, whose prophetic qualities have been portrayed in another chapter, for various birds came to be considered "fortunate" or "unfortunate," from the point of view of the seeker after supernal guidance, either on account of their own characteristics or according to the place and manner of their appearance; hence the same species might, at different times, foretell contrary events. Let me quote here a succinct statement from *The Encyclopedia Londonensis,* published in the early part of the 18th century:

If a flock of various birds came flying about any man it was an excellent omen. The eagle was particularly observed for drawing omens; when it was observed to be brisk and lively, and especially if, during its sportiveness, it flew from the right hand to the left, it was one of the best omens that the gods could give. Respecting vultures there are different opinions, both among the Greek and the Roman authors; by some they are represented as birds of lucky omen, while Aristotle and Pliny reckon them among the unlucky birds. If the hawk was seen seizing and devouring her prey, it portended death; but if the prey escaped deliverance from danger was portended. Swallows wherever and under whatever circumstances they were seen were unlucky birds; before the defeat of Pyrrhus and Antony they appeared on the tent of the former and the ship of the latter; and, by dispiriting their minds, probably prepared the way for their subsequent disasters. In every part of Greece except Athens, owls were regarded as unlucky birds; but at Athens, being sacred to Minerva, they were looked upon as omens of victory and success. The swan, being an omen of fair weather, was deemed a lucky bird by mariners.

The most inauspicious omens were given by ravens, but the degree of misfortune which they were supposed to portend depended, in some measure, in their appearing on the right hand or the left; if they came croaking on the right hand it was a tolerably good omen; but if on the left a very bad one. . . . The crow appearing [at a wedding] denoted long life to the married pair, if it appeared with its mate; but if it was seen single separation and sorrow were portended. Whence it was customary at nuptials for the maids to watch that none of these birds coming singly should disturb the solemnity.

It was hardly to be expected that the comprehension of all this science of soothsaying should belong to ordinary mortals; and therefore there arose early in its development certain clever "wise men" who declared themselves endowed with magical power to understand the language of birds, and to interpret both their chatter and their actions. Thus originated the profession of *augury,* a word that spells "bird-talk" in its root-meaning, with its later product *auspices,* or "bird-viewers." The augur originally was a priest (or a magician, if you prefer that term) who listened to what the birds said; and the auspex was another who watched what they did, or examined their entrails to observe anything abnormal that he might construe as an answer to prayer, or interpreted something else in the nature of an omen from this or that divinity, or from all the gods together.

I need not describe the elaborate rites and ceremonies that came to be associated with the practice of this kind of divination (ornithomancy), especially under the revered and powerful College of Augurs that practically ruled the Roman Republic, even in the Augustan age, for it will suffice to direct attention to a few features.

Birds were distinguished by the Roman augurs as *oscines* or *alites,* "talkers" and "flyers." The oscines were birds that gave signs by their cry as well as by flight, such as ravens, owls and crows. The alites included birds like eagles and vultures, which gave signs by their manner of flying. The quarter of the heavens in which they appeared, and their position relative to that of the observer, were most important factors in determining the significance of the supposed message, as has been extensively explained in an earlier chapter of this book.

This science or business of bird-divination, for it was both, was of prehistoric antiquity. Plutarch [94] records that Romulus and Remus, the fabled founders of the Latin race began their eventful life under a wild fig-tree, where a she-wolf nursed them, and a woodpecker constantly fed and watched over them. "These creatures," Plutarch remarks, "are esteemed holy to the god Mars—the woodpecker the Latins still especially worship and honor. Romulus became skilled in divination, and first carried the *lituus,* or diviner's staff, a crooked rod with which soothsayers indicated the quarters of the heavens when observing the flight of birds."

> Among the Romans not a bird
> Without a prophecy was heard.
> Fortunes of empire often hung
> On the magician magpie's tongue,
> And every crow was to the state
> A sure interpreter of fate.—*Churchill.*

The peculiar province of the auspices, or bird-inspecters, was to seek the will of the gods as to some contemplated act or policy by watching the behavior of the sacred chickens, cared for by an official called *pullarius.* "If the chickens came too slowly out of the cage, or would not feed, it was a bad omen; but if they fed greedily, so that some part of their food fell and struck the ground, it was deemed an excellent omen."—and so forth and so forth.

It is rather engaging to inquire why the humble barnyard fowl was used for so momentous a function. Partly, no doubt, because it was the most convenient kind of bird to keep and propagate in captivity, and therefore would always be at hand when wanted (and in case the prophecy-demand was light an occasional pullet for the official pot would not be missed!), but also because its witlessness made it dependable. A devotee of this way of omen-catching would explain that of course the bird was unconscious of the part it played; that its mind was a mere receptacle of divine impulses to act in a certain way, the significance of which the auspex understood and reported. If that theory is true, it follows that the more empty-headed the "medium" is the better, for it would then have fewer ideas of its own to short-circuit the inspired impulses. This view has, in fact, influenced ignorant folks everywhere in their conclusion that men who were witless, or crazy, or had lost their mentality in a trance, were "possessed," mostly by devils but sometimes by good "spirits" which had found a mind "swept and garnished," as St. Luke said, and had become vocal tenants; whence, it was argued, no human rationality interfered with the transmission of the message, and men must accept what the tongues uttered as inspired words. "Out of the mouths of babes and sucklings came forth praise" that was praise indeed, because the infants knew not what they said. That was the reason Balaam listened with so much respect to the warning spoken by his ass; and many a preaching ass since has had a similar reward for articulate braying.

One more consideration suggests itself. The ominous flock kept by the pullarius contained both cocks and hens; and the cock, as a bird of the sun, has been "sacred" from prehistoric antiquity in that primitive nature-worship from which the Greco-Romans were by no means free. "It is not improbable," we are assured by Houghton [95] "that the sacrificial rites and consultation by augury, in which cooks figured among the Romans, came originally from Babylonia ... I think that the figure [in a seal] of a cock perched on an altar before a priest making his offerings ... represents the bird in this capacity as a soothsayer." In fact, a whole department of the science of augury was known as alectromancy, in which a barnyard cock was the agent or medium of inspiration.

These practices—which were entirely void of morality—are a curious index of the mental barbarism of the early Greeks and Romans, for they are quite on a level with the ideas and doings of savages now.

With the advance in knowledge and enlightenment culminating in the philosophy of Cicero and his skeptical contemporaries, both faith and practice in this childish consultation of chickens and crows disappeared, or descended to be merely a political sop for the credulous populace. Even this passed away when superstitious paganism faded out of the religion of mankind in Europe, or, more exactly, it became changed into a faith in weather prophecy by noticing the behavior of birds and other animals; but these prognostications are based not on a supposed message from the gods but on deductions from observation and experience. Let us see how far this modern method of augury is of service as a sort of home-made Weather Bureau—we will, as it were, study the genesis of the Rain-bird. It began early. Aristophanes tells us, of the Greeks:

> From birds in sailing men instruction take
> Now lie in port, now sail, and profit make.

The proprietor of Gardiner's Island, at the eastern end of Long Island, New York, where fish-hawks then abounded, and always since have been under protection, told Alexander Wilson [46] many facts of interest respecting their habits, among others the following:

They are sometimes seen high in the air, sailing and cutting strange gambols, with loud vociferations, darting down several hundred feet perpendicularly, frequently with part of a fish in one claw, which they seem proud of, and to claim "high hook," as the fishermen call him who takes the greatest number. On these occasions they serve as a barometer to foretell the changes of the atmosphere; for when the fish-hawks are thus sailing high in air, in circles, it is universally believed to prognosticate a change of weather, often a thunder-storm in a few hours. On the faith of the certainty of these signs the experienced coaster wisely prepares for the expected storm, and is rarely mistaken.

It would be hard to find a better epitome of the "signs" given by birds to the weather-prophet. Similar behavior in sea-gulls is interpreted in the same way: but in most cases high flight is said to denote continuance of fine weather, and in general there is good sense in that view, because, as a rule, bad weather descends upon us from the higher strata of the atmosphere, and birds up there would be the first to feel its approach. Hence the joyous greeting, "Everything is lovely and the goose honks (not 'hangs') high." Sailors have a rhyme—

When men-of-war-hawks fly high, 't is a sign of clear sky;
When they fly low prepare for a blow.

This point is made in particular in respect to swallows of various kinds, which are regarded in most countries as presaging rain when they all go skimming along close to the ground; but it was pure fancy that expanded this warning into the senseless couplet

When the swallow buildeth low
You can safely reap and sow.

That is, I suppose, the season will then furnish rain
enough for a good crop.   The same thing is sung of
swans.   But even the swallows cannot be depended on as
indicators, for in late summer and autumn they are more
likely to skim along the ground and over ponds than to
go anywhere else; and, as showing the uncertainty in
men's minds in this matter, or else how signs change with
locality, it may be mentioned that in Argentina swallows
are held to indicate coming storms not by low but by elevated flight.   Thus the naturalist Hudson [44] writes of the
musical martin (Progne), familiar about Buenos Ayres:
"It is . . . . the naturalist's barometer, as whenever, the
atmosphere being clear and dry, the progne perches on
the weathercock or lightning-rod, on the highest points of
the house-top, or on the topmost twig of some lofty tree,
chanting its incantation, cloudy weather and rain will
surely follow within twenty-four hours."

None of the host of sayings, of which you may read
hundreds in the publications of the United States Weather
Service, and in such collections of odd lore as *Gleanings
for the Curious*,[96] that pretend to foretell the character of
a whole season from what birds do, are worth credence.
For example, some declare that "a dry summer will follow when birds build their nests in exposed places," on
the theory, I suppose, that the builders will have no fear
of getting wet; and

> If birds in the autumn grow tame,
> The winter will be cold for game.

One important exception to this kind of nonsense may
be made, however, for in certain circumstances it is fair
to accept from our American birds a broad hint as to the
character of the approaching winter.   Experience con-

vinces us that an unusually early arrival of migratory birds from the north indicates an extra cold winter to follow.   Several northwestern sayings about ducks and geese tell us that whenever they leave Lake Superior noticeably earlier than is their wont; or fly southward straight and fast, not lingering near accustomed halting-places, then a severe season is to be anticipated.   In the sum this is logical, for this reason:

Birds whose home is in the far North—and several species go to the extreme limit of arctic lands to make their nests—must quit those desolate coasts as soon as chilling rains, snow-storms, and frost begin to kill the insects, bury the plants and freeze the streams, thus cutting off food-supplies; and they must keep ahead of those famine-producing conditions as they travel southward toward their winter-resorts in a more hospitable zone. On the average, their arrival in the United States will be nearly on the same date year after year.

It sometimes happens, however, that winter will pounce upon the arctic border of the continent days or weeks earlier than usual, and the cold and snowfall will exceed the normal quantity.   In such circumstances the birds must make their escape more hastily than ordinarily, and will come down across the Canadian border in larger and more hurrying companies, very likely accompanied by such species as snow-birds, crossbills, pine finches and evening grosbeaks, which in general pass the winter somewhat to the north of our boundary.   Excessive cold in the far North is almost certain to influence southern Canada and the northern states, and it is therefore safe to conclude, when we witness this behavior of migratory birds, that a winter of exceptional severity has set in at the north and is in store for us.   But the prophets are

ourselves—not the birds! They are dealing with dangerous conditions, and leave it to us to do the theorizing.

One feature of the behavior of the fish-hawks in Wilson's story was their restlessness, taken by fishermen to
betoken a rising storm. There may be some value in this
"sign," since it is noted in many other cases. Dozens of
proverbs mention as indications various unusual actions
noticeable in poultry, such as crowing at odd times, clap-
pings of the wings, rolling in the dust, standing about in a
distraught kind of way, a tendency to flocking, and so
forth. Many popular sayings tell us that both barnyard
fowls and wild birds become very noisy before an unfavorable change in the weather.

> When the peacock loudly bawls
> Soon we'll have both rain and squalls,

is one such. Virgil's statement that "the owl" screeches
unduly at such a time is supported by modern testimony.

A reasonable explanation of this uneasiness is that it
is the effect of that increased electrical tension in the atmosphere that often precedes a shower, to which small
creatures are perhaps more sensitive than are men and
large animals. It will not do, then, to reject *all* the
weather-signs popularly alleged to be given by animals.

At the same time, as has been suggested, much of the
current weather-prophecy relating to animals is silly,
such, for example, that a solitary turkey-buzzard seen at
a great altitude indicates rain; that blackbirds' notes are
very shrill before rain; that there will be no rain the day
a heron flies down the creek; that when woodpeckers peck
low on the tree-trunks expect a hard winter. These, and
many other nonsensical maxims, are in fact spurious.
Most of them, no doubt, were uttered originally in jest,

or as a whimsical answer to some inquisitive child, then repeated as amusing, and finally quoted seriously. Others have been brought to us from the old world by early farmer-immigrants—French in Canada, Louisiana and New England, Dutch in New York, Swedish and German in New Jersey and Pennsylvania, Spanish in the Southwest, and so on—and have been applied to our native birds, where often they fail to fit. A saw that perhaps had some value when told of the European robin or blackbird, is ludicrously inappropriate when said of our blackbirds and robins, which are totally different in nature and habits.

One of the most venerable of these worthless prognostics, and one that very likely is a relic of Roman auspices, twenty-five centuries ago, is that of the goose-bone:

"To read the winter of any year take the breast-bone of a goose hatched during the preceding spring. The bone is translucent, and it will be found to be colored and spotted. The dark color and heavy spots indicate cold. If the spots are of light shade, and transparent, wet weather, rain or snow, may be looked for.

"If the November goose-bone be thick,
So will the winter weather be;
If the November goose-bone be thin,
So will the winter weather be."

One need not wonder at the indignant refusal of hardheaded commanders of old who refused to let their strategy or tactics to be interfered with by alarmed priests who reported unfavorable auguries from dissected hens. Eusebius records the legend that a bird was presented to Alexander the Macedonian when on the point of setting out for the Red Sea, in order that he might read the auguries according to custom. Alexander killed the bird by an arrow, saying, "What folly is this? How could a bird that could not foresee its death by this arrow, predict the fortunes of our journey?" The shocked bystanders might have replied, of course, that the poor creature had no such knowledge in itself, but was merely the blank on which divine intelligence was written; but the chances are that they held their tongues! Plutarch mentions many a case in which commanders construed the "omens" in a way contrary to the priestly interpretation, in order to carry out some plan that could not be delayed, and yet conciliate the superstitious soldiers.

It will have been noticed that most of the prophecies learned from birds relate to coming rain or bad weather, and winter rather than summer. In *The Strange Metamorphosis of Man* (1634), as quoted by Brewer,[34] speaking of the goose, we read: "She is no witch or astrologer, . . . but she hath a shrewd guesse of rainie weather, being as good as an almanac to some that beleeve in her." Men generally seem more desirous of ascertaining the evil than the good that may be in store for them. The feeling is, perhaps, that if we knew of dangers ahead we might prepare for them, but that in fair days we can take care of ourselves. Almost every country has some particular "rain-bird" whose cry is supposed to foretell showers. In England it is the green woodpecker, or yaffle; in Malaya a broadbill; in some parts of this country the spotted sandpiper, or tipup; but *everywhere* some sort of cuckoo is called "rain-bird" or "rain-crow," although the various cuckoos of America, Europe, and the Orient, differ widely in appearance, habits and voice.

Why should peoples so dissimilar and widely scattered attribute to this very diverse cuckoo family the quality of "rain-birds" more than to another family? I can only

believe that it denotes the survival of a very ancient
Oriental notion, whose significance was very real in a
symbolic way to the primitive people among whom it
originated locally, but has now been utterly forgotten.

Plunging into the thickets of comparative mythology,
hoping to pluck a few fruity facts for our pains, we find
that in Hindoo myths the cuckoo stands as a symbol of
the sun when hidden behind clouds, that is, for a rainy
condition of the sky; furthermore that this bird has a
reputation for possessing exceeding wisdom surpassing
that of other birds, all of which are fabled to be supernaturally wise: and that it knew not only things present
but things to come. It was, in fact, in the opinion of the
ancient Hindoos, a prophetic bird of unrivalled vatic
ability. The Greeks thought their own cuckoo had inherited some of these qualities, for they made it one of
the birds in the Olympian aviary of Zeus, who, please remember, was the pluvial god.

Plainly this rainy-day character was given to the bird
through the circumstance that in southern Asia, as in
southern Europe, the cuckoo is one of the earliest and
quite the most conspicuous of spring-birds—and the
spring is the rainy season. In early days farmers had
little knowledge of a calendar. They sowed and reaped
when it seemed fitting to do so. The coming of the cuckoo
coincided with experience, and came to be their almanac-
date for certain operations—*a signal convenient in advice
to the young, or to a newcomer;* and as a rule hoped-for
showers followed the bird's advent. In the same way
old-fashioned Pennsylvania farmers used to connect corn-
planting time and the first-heard singing of the brown
thrasher.

Hesiod instructed his rural countrymen that if "it

should happen to rain three days in succession when the cuckoo sings among the oak-trees, then late sowing will be as good as early sowing"—doubtless good agricultural counsel. Not more than a century ago English farmers thought it necessary to sow barley when the earliest note of the cuckoo was heard in order to insure a full crop. Mr. Friend [11] reasons thus about this: "As the cuckoo only returns to our shores at a certain time, it has been customary to predict from his appearance what kind of season will follow; and farmers have in all ages placed great reliance on omens of weather and crops drawn from this source. . . . In Berwickshire those oats which are sown after the first of April are called 'gowk's' [cuckoo's] oats . . .

> Cuckoo oats and wood cock hay
> Make a farmer run away.

If the spring is so backward that the oats cannot be sown until the cuckoo is heard, or the autumn so wet that the hay cannot be gathered in until the woodcocks come over, the farmer is sure to suffer great loss."

So much for these old maxims; and when British or Italian immigrants became colonists in America, and found cuckoos here, they continued the sayings, regardless of difference in climate and other circumstances. Our species are not early migrants in spring, are poor guides for planters, and seem to have no prophetic gift, yet they are rain-birds because their ancestral relatives in India were such 3,000 years ago.

CHAPTER XII

A PRIMITIVE VIEW OF THE ORIGIN OF SPECIES

I F anyone should ask you how a particular bird came to be blue or red or streaked, or how it happened that birds in general differ in colors and other features, "each after its kind," in other words how specific distinctions came about, you, a liberal-minded and well-read person, would undoubtedly answer that each and all "developed" these specific characteristics. You might go on to explain that they resulted from the combined influences of natural and sexual selection, to the latter of which birds are supposed to be especially susceptible, and thereby show yourself a good Darwinist.

But primitive thinkers, like children, are not evolutionists but creationists. They believe that things were made as they are: if so, somebody made them. They are convinced that no person like themselves or any of their acquaintances could do it, so they attribute the feat to some being with superhuman powers. This being is almost always the mythical ancestor, pristine instructor or "culture-hero," of the nation, tribe or clan to which the thinker belongs; and it is perfectly natural and a matter of course to assume that he had magical functions and supernatural powers. Next, some genius invents a story to fit the case, and as anything is possible to such a being as the hero it is adopted and passed into the tribal history that the elders recount by the evening fire, and that everybody accepts without suspicion or criticism. The Hebrews, for example, said that Adam, their "first man," "gave names to all cattle, and to the fowl of the air, and to every beast of the field; . . . and whatsoever Adam called every living creature that was the name thereof." As to his reasons for giving this name to one creature and another to that, it has been whimsically explained that he called the raccoon that because "it looked like a 'coon' " —quite as good a reason as the legend requires.

Now the two questions at the beginning of this chapter were, in fact, asked by a great variety of our aboriginal Americans, the red Indians, and undoubtedly by the aborigines of most other countries; but for the present let us stick to North America.

When some bright-witted, inquisitive Iroquois youngster, hearing and seeing many birds on a soft June morning, asked his mother how it happened that they wore such a diversity of plumages, she told him this story: In the beginning the birds were naked, but some of them became ashamed, and cried for coverings. (In those days, of course, birds talked with one another, and even with the wiser sort of men.) They were told that their suits were ready but were a long way off. At last the turkey-buzzard was persuaded to go and get them. He had been a clean bird, but during the long journey had to eat much carrion and filth, hence his present nature. Guided by the gods he reached the store of plumages, and selfishly chose for himself the most beautifully colored dress, but as he found he could not fly in it he was forced to take his present one, which enables him to soar most gracefully. Finally he brought their varied suits to the other birds.

The Iroquois lad would be quite satisfied with this

account of the matter; but a boy on the opposite side of
the continent would get a very different explanation. He
would be told that Raven did it. Raven—or the raven—
was the mythical ancestor or culture hero, as ethnologists
would say, of the foremost clan of the Tlingit tribe,
whose territory was in southern Alaska. He was present
at the making of the world and its people, and did many
marvellous things. While he was at Sitka arranging
affairs in the new world he assigned to all the birds, one
by one, the place of their resort and their habits, and his
good nature is shown by the fact that to the robin and
the hummingbird he assigned the duty of giving pleasure
to men, the former by its song and the latter by its beauty.
By and by the birds dressed one another in different ways,
so that they might easily be recognized apart. They tied
the hair of the bluejay up high with a string, put a striped
coat on the little woodpecker, and so on. The Kwakiutl
coastal Indians of British Columbia deny this, however.
They say the birds did not select their own costumes, but
that one of their ancestors painted all the birds he found
at a certain place. When he reached the cormorant his
colors were exhausted and he had only charcoal left, hence
the cormorant is wholly black.

George Keith,[99] who in 1807 was a fur-trader on the
Mackenzie River, gathered and recorded much valuable
material as to the customs and ideas of the Beaver
Indians of that region, who belonged to the Ojibway
family. In one of his stories Keith gives the Indians' explanation of how certain birds got their colors: it was
during the time of a great flood. At that period all birds
were white, but l'épervier (the sharp-shinned hawk),
l'émerillon (the goshawk), and l'canard de France
(mallard) agreed to change to a plumage in colors—how

it was to be done the Indians were unable to say. The story proceeds:

Immediately after this event the corbeau [raven] made his appearance. "Come," says l'epervier to the corbeau, "would you not wish to have a coat like mine?" "Hold your tongue!" rejoined the corbeau. "With your crooked bill is not white handsomer than any other color?" The others argued with the corbeau to consent, but he remained inflexible, which so exasperated l'epervier and the others that they determined to avenge this affront, and each taking a burnt coal in his bill they blacked him all over. The corbeau, enraged at this treatment, and determined not to be singular, espied a flock of étourneaux [blackbirds] and, without shaking off the black dust of his feathers, threw himself amongst them and bespattered them all over with black, which is the reason for their still retaining this color.

Further south, on Puget Sound, once lived the tribe of Twanas, who held that in former times men painted themselves in various hues, whereupon Dokblatt, their culture-hero, who notoriously was fond of changing things, turned these men into birds, which explains the present diversity in avian plumage.

The Arawaks of Venezuela, however, account for this matter by saying that the birds obtained their gay feathers by selecting parts of a huge, gaudily colored water-snake that the cormorant killed for them by diving into the water; yet the cormorant, with great modesty, kept for himself only the snake's head, which was blackish.

Most explanatory stories concern single kinds of birds, and inform us how they got the peculiar features by which we identify them with their names; and here we get back to the nearctic raven. A history of the exploits of this personage—bird, bird-man or bird-god—who is the hero of more tales than any other of the giants that flourished in the formative period of the northern Indian's world, would fill a big book. "The creator of all things and the benefactor of man was the great raven called by the Thlingit Yel, Yeshil or Yeatl, and by the Haida Ne-kil-stlas. He was not exactly an ordinary bird but had . . . many human attributes, and the power of transforming himself into anything in the world. His coat of feathers could be put on or taken off at will like a garment, and he could assume any character whatever. He existed before his birth, never grows old, and will never die." So Mr. (now Admiral) Niblack, U. S. N., characterized this supreme magician;[100] and Dr. E. W. Nelson [101] adds that this creation-legend is believed by the Eskimos from the Kuskoquim River in southern Alaska northward to Bering Strait, and thence eastward all along the Arctic Coast. The purely mythological relation of this widely revered northwestern raven is thus summarized by Brinton [27]:

This father of the race is represented as a mighty bird, called Yel, or Yale, or Orelbale, from the root [Athabascan] *ell,* a term they apply to everything supernatural. He took to wife a daughter of the Sun (the Woman of Light), and by her begat the race of men. He formed the dry land for a place for them to live upon, and stocked the rivers with salmon that they might have food. When he enters his nest it is day, but when he leaves it it is night; or, according to another myth, he has two women for wives, the one of whom makes the day, the other the night. In the beginning Yel was white in plumage, but he had an enemy . . . by whose machinations he was turned black. Yel is further represented as the god of the winds and storms, and of the thunder and lightning.

It is plain that in studying the deeds and accidents attributed to this American member of the sun-born "fabulous flock" described in another chapter, it is often difficult to separate Raven the demigod, from the sable, kawing, cunning bird so conspicuous all over northern Canada; and in this respect Yel differs from Rukh, Simurgh, and the other similar figments of Oriental fancies, in that he is modelled upon a real bird, rather than on something utterly unknown to earthly ornithology.

A favorite tale with many variants describes how the cormorant lost its voice. As the Haidas of Queen Charlotte Islands tell it, Raven once invited the cormorant to go a-fishing with him. The cormorant went, and naturally caught many fish, while the Raven took none. Then Raven, angry made the cormorant stick out its tongue. "There is something on it," quoth Raven, and pulled the tongue out by the roots; and that is why cormorants have no voice.*

Here Raven is plainly the supernatural, irresponsible being of Totemic importance, who often presented himself as a man or in some other form, for he could assume any shape he liked. Thus the Hudson Bay Eskimos relate that Raven was a man who loudly cautioned persons when moving a village-camp not to forget the deer-skin under-blanket called "kak": so he got that nickname, and ravens still fly about fussily calling *kak! kak!* The Tlingits also have a story in which Raven begins the action as a man, and ends plain bird—an outwitted one at that. Raven was in a house and played a trick on Petrel, then tried to get away by flying up through the smoke-hole in the

* The cormorant was once a wool-merchant. He entered into a partnership with the bramble and the bat, and they freighted a large ship with wool. She was wrecked and the firm became bankrupt. Since that disaster the bat skulks about until midnight to avoid his creditors, the cormorant is forever diving into the deep to discover its foundered vessel, while the bramble seizes hold of every passing sheep to make up the firm's loss by stealing the wool. This is an ancient European story quite as silly as the Haida one.

roof, but got stuck there. Seeing this Petrel built a birch-wood fire under him, so as to make much smoke. The raven was white before that time, but the smudge blackened him forever.

The Greenland Eskimos account for the change in the raven from white to black by the story of its vexing the snow-owl, which was its fast friend in the ancient days before marvels became marvellous. One day the raven made a new dress, dappled black and white (the summer plumage), for the owl, which in return fashioned a pair of whalebone boots for the raven, and also a white dress, as was proper for ravens at that time; but the raven would not stay quiet while it was tried on. The owl shouted angrily, "Sit still or I shall pour the lamp over you!" Nevertheless the bird kept hopping about until the owl, out of patience, picked up the soapstone saucer-lamp and drenched him with the sooty lamp-oil. Since then the ever-restless raven has been black all over.

The Haidas say that the crow likewise was originally white, and that on one occasion Raven turned it black as a spiteful sort of joke.

It is interesting to recall that in classic myth ravens were once as white as swans and as large; but one day a raven told his patron, Apollo, that Coronis, a Thessalian nymph whom he passionately loved, was faithless, where-upon the god shot the nymph with his dart, but hating the telltale bird

> . . . he blacked the raven o'er
> And bid him prate in his white plumes no more,

as Ovid sings in Addison's translation. Some accounts say that one of Odin's messenger-ravens was white. To this day the peasants about Brescia, in Italy, speak of January 30 and 31, and February 1, as "blackbird days," and explained that many years ago the local blackbirds were white; but in one hard winter it was so cold these thrushes were compelled to take refuge in chimneys, and ever since have worn a sooty plumage.

This belief that the sable brotherhood of the crow-tribe was once white seems to be universal, and perhaps arises in the equally general, albeit somewhat childish, feeling that nothing is as it used to be; and coupled with this is the similarly common feeling that every event or condition ought to be accounted for. Thus we get a glimpse at the psychology in these primitive stories of the reason why this and that animal is as we see it. Skeat [7] found among the Malays, for example, a legend that in the days of King Solomon the argus pheasant was dowdily dressed, and it besought the crow to paint its plumage in splendid colors. The crow complied and gave the pheasant its present beautifully variegated costume; but when the artist asked for a similar service toward itself from the pheasant the latter not only refused but spilt a bottle of ink over the crow.

To return to the erratic, and usually mischievous career of Yel, the Northwestern (raven) culture-hero, it is remembered that often, kindly or unkindly, he changed sundry birds besides owls from something else into their present form. For example, he sent a hawk into the Tlingit country after fire. Previously the hawk's bill had been long, but in bringing the fire this long beak was burned short, and has ever remained so. Nelson [101] learned from Alaskan Eskimos why the short-eared owl has so diminutive a beak, nearly hidden in the feathers of the flat face. This owl, it appears, was once a little girl who lived in a village by the lower Yukon. "She was changed by magic into a bird with a long bill, and became so frightened that she sprang up and flew off in an erratic way until she struck the side of a house, flattening her beak and face so that she became just as the owls are seen to-day."

Raven made woodpeckers (red-shafted flickers) out of the blood that gushed from his nose after he had bruised it; and Haida fishermen now tie scarlet flicker feathers to their halibut hooks "for luck." Their neighbors, the Clalams, thought it better to use a piece of kingfisher skin —and in my opinion their reasoning was the sounder of the two. Perhaps it was Raven whom the Tshimshian Indians of Nass River meant when they spoke of "Giant's" treatment of the gulls. The Giant, as Professor Boaz heard it designated, had some oolachans (smelts) and stuck them on sticks to roast by his fire. "When they were done a gull appeared over the Giant. Then the Giant called him 'Little Gull.' Then many gulls came, which ate all the Giant's oolachans. They said while they were eating it *qana, qana, qana!* Then he was sad. Therefore he took the gulls and threw them into the fireplace, and ever since the tips of their wings have been black."

The culture-hero of the Twana Indians of the Puget Sound region was Dokibat, as has been mentioned, who had a habit of changing things, turning men into stones or birds, and so forth. A boy hearing that he was coming, and fearing some unpleasant transformation, ran away, carrying with him a water-box (used in canoe-journeys by sea) with water in it. The water shaking about sounded somewhat like *pu-pu-pu* when repeated rapidly; but as the boy ran wings came to him and he began to fly, and the noise in the box sounded like the cooing of the wood-dove, which the Twans called "hum-o." A man was pounding against a cedar-tree. Dokibat came along and asked him what he was doing. "Trying to break or split this tree," was the answer. Dokibat said: "You may stop and go away, and I will help you." As the woodman went wings came to him, also a long bill and a strong head, and he became a woodpecker.

How the woodpecker got the red mark on the back of its head, which is a characteristic of most species, is explained by the Algonkins thus, according to Schoolcraft:[102] Manabozho, the renowned culture-hero of the Ojibways and their relatives, made a campaign against the Shining Manito, and at last, finding him in his lair, a mortal combat began. At length Manabozho had left only three arrows, and the fight was going against him. Ma-ma, the woodpecker, cried out: "Shoot him at the base of the scalp-lock; it is his only vulnerable spot!" (The Indians have many stories turning on this point, and reminding us of that of Achilles.) Then with the third and last arrow Manabozho hit the fatal spot, and taking the scalp of the Shining Manito as a trophy he rubbed blood from it on the woodpecker's head, which remains red in his descendants. That the redheaded species (*Melanerpes torquatus*), abundant in summer in the Ojibway country, is meant here is evident from the further statement that its red feathers were thereafter regarded as symbols of valor, and were chosen to ornament the warriors' pipes, for no other woodpecker of the region could furnish enough such feathers to answer the purpose.

The Menominees, of southern Wisconsin, had a different story relating to the scarlet crest of another kind of woodpecker. They say that Ball-carrier, who was a bad-tempered sort of fellow among their demigods, promised the logcock, or big black woodpecker of the forest, that if he would kill a certain Cannibal-Woman he should have a piece of her scalp with its lock of red hair. So the bird rushed at her and drove his chisel-like beak into her heart. Then Ball-carrier gave her red scalp-lock to the logcock, which placed it on his own head, as one may see now. In Indo-European mythology woodpeckers figure among lightning-birds, and the red mark on their heads is deemed the badge of their office.

The need of accounting for notable features like this in animals seems to have appealed to all sorts of people, all around the world, in each case according to local ideas. Thus an Arabic tradition current in Palestine accounts for the fork in the tail of swallows by the fact that a bird of this species baffled a scheme of the Old Serpent (Eblis) in Paradise, whereupon the serpent struck at it, but succeeded only in biting out a notch in the middle of its tail. Another example: Nigerian negros say that the vulture got its bald head by malicious transference of a disease with which a green pigeon had been suffering—a native guess at the filth-bacteria to which modern zoologists attribute the nakedness! Oddly enough, a folk-tale in Louisiana, related by Fortier,[106] similarly explains the baldness of our turkey-buzzard by saying it came from a pan of hot ashes thrown at the vulture's head in revenge for an injury it had committed on a rabbit—and "buzzards never eat bones of rabbits."

The Iowas account for the peculiar baldness of this bird by a long story recounted by Spence[12] in which their mythical hero Ictinike figures. Ictinike asked a buzzard to carry him toward a certain place. The crafty bird consented, but presently dropped him in a tall hollow tree. Ictinike was wearing 'coonskins, and when presently some persons came along he thrust their tails through cracks in the trunk. Three women, thinking that raccoons had become imprisoned in the tree, cut a hole to capture them, whereupon Ictinike came out and the women ran away. Then Ictinike lay down wrapped in his furs as if asleep, and an eagle, a crow, and a magpie came and began pecking at him. The buzzard, thinking this meant a feast, rushed down from the sky, and Ictinike jumped up and tore off its scalp, since which the buzzard has been bald.

But many explanations of why birds are now so or so make no mention of Ravens or Ictinikes, but just tell you the fact. Thus the Eskimos of northwestern Alaska relate that one autumn day very long ago the cranes prepared to go southward. As they were gathered in a great flock they saw a beautiful girl standing alone near a village. Admiring her greatly, the cranes gathered about her, and lifting her on their wide-spread wings bore her far up and away. While the cranes were taking her aloft their brethren circled about below her so closely that she could not fall, and with hoarse cries drowned her screams for help. So she was swept away into the sky, and never seen again. Always since that time the cranes have circled about in autumn, uttering loud cries.

The Hudson Bay Eskimos tell their boys and girls when they see the funny little guillemots by the sea-cliffs and ask about them, that once a lot of children were playing near the brink of such a precipice. Their noisy shouts disturbed a band of seal-hunters on the strand below; and one of the men exclaimed, "I wish the cliff would topple over and bury those noisy children!" In a moment the height did so, and the poor infants fell among the rocks below. There they were changed into guillemots and dwell to this day on the crags at the edge of the sea.

Another juvenile story explains that the swallows became what they are by a change from Eskimo children who were making "play-house" igloos of mud on the top of a cliff. To this day the swallows come every summer and fix their mud nests to the rocks, recalling their childish joy in the previous state of their existence. Hence the Eskimo children particularly love to watch these birds in their "igluiaks," which are said not to be molested by the predatory ravens.

Once a long war was fought between the brants and the herons, according to a Tlingit legend, but at last the swans intervened and a peace was arranged. To celebrate it the herons indulged in much dancing, and have been dancers ever since. I am inclined to think this another crane legend, because the few herons known in the Tlingit country do not indulge in such antics, whereas the cranes do "dance" a great deal in the mating-season. These Indians, by the way, say that they learned the use of pickaxes by watching a heron strike the ground with its beak; and the suggestion of snowshoes was caught from the ptarmigan, on whose feet grow in winter expansions of the toes that serve to make it easier for the bird to walk on snow.

The ruffed grouse, the Ojibways declare, was marked with eleven spots on its tail to remind him of the time when he wouldn't do as he was told, and had to fast eleven days as a punishment. On the other hand Manabozho rewarded the kingfisher for some useful information by hanging a medal (in color) about its neck; but in bestowing the medal Manabozho snatched at the king-

fisher's head, intending to twist it off—a very characteristic dodge of these treacherous old culture-heroes—but
only rumpled the bird's crest, so that it has been a ragged
sort of headdress ever since.

The extinct Chitimacha Indians of northern Louisiana
had a tale that a man set the marshes on fire, and a little
bird uprose through the smoke and remonstrated. The
man was angry and threw a shell at the bird, which
wounded its wings and made them bleed, and thus the
red-winged blackbird got its scarlet shoulders.

A familiar and active little shrike of the northern
border of South America is the kiskadee, with a conspicuous white mark on its head. The Arawaks say that
this radiant little songster, which has the same sort of
fierce hostility to hawks and other large birds as distinguishes our doughty kingbird, got tired of a war that
was going on among the animals, put a white bandage
around its head and pretended to be sick. The war
halted long enough to expose the fraud of the little mal-
ingerer, and kiskadees were sentenced to wear the white
bandage perpetually.

Arawak story-tellers also relate that the trumpeter
(Psophia) and a kingfisher quarrelled over the spoils of
war, and knocked each other into the ashes, which accounts for the gray of their plumage. The nakedness of
the trumpeter's legs is owing to his stepping into an
ant's nest, and getting them picked clean. The owl discovered a package among the spoil of the war that contained only darkness, since which that bird cannot endure
daylight. It is interesting to compare with this the ad-
venture of the trumpeter current among the Maquiritares,
which is related elsewhere.

So the stories go on. The Pimas, for example, believe

that the mountain bluebird was originally an unlovely gray, but acquired its present exquisite azure coat by bathing in a certain lake of blue water that had neither inlet nor outlet. It bathed in this regularly for four mornings. On the fourth morning it shed all its plumage and came out with the skin bare; but on the fifth morning it emerged from its bath with a coat of blue.

This tradition is somewhat sentimental, as befits the sweetly warbling and beloved bluebird, which is not only a favorite, but has a certain sacredness in the southwest; but often, in the majority of cases perhaps, a rough humor tinges the history. Thus Manabush, a mythical ancestor of the Menominees, once assembled all the birds by a subterfuge, and then killed several. The little grebe, or "hell-diver," was one of those chosen for death, and as it was a poor runner it was easily caught. Manabush said contemptuously, "I won't kill you, but you shall always have red eyes and be the laughing-stock of all the birds." With that he gave the poor bird a kick, sending it far out into Lake Michigan and knocking off its tail, so that the hell-diver is red-eyed and almost tailless to this day.

I have restricted this chapter mainly to examples from the folklore of the American Indians, but, were there not danger of becoming tedious, many more might be quoted from the fireside tales of other countries, especially Africa. African traditions, however, can hardly be held to account for the following explanations by some Southern darkies as given by Martha Young [2]:

The bluejay was yoked into a plow by the sparrow, and the necklace-like mark on his breast is the mark left by the yoke worn in this degrading service.

The buzzard originally had a "fine plume sweepin' from de

top of his head," but lost it in a quarrel with a dog. "Sense dat day Buzzard don't never miss fust pickin' out de eye of ev'thing that he gwine eat," so that it cannot see to resist if it is not quite dead.

Darkies say that the hummingbird lost her voice—"she choke her voice clean out of her wid honey"—through being so greedy when she first discovered the honey in flowers, by reason of contracting a "swimmin' in de head" by incessant whirling, as her poising on wings seems to the negroes. "She hav a notion now that she los' her voice . . . deep in some flower. She's al'a'rs lookin' fer dat los' voice. Flash in dis flower! Dash in dat flower! But she'll nuvver, nuvver fin' it."

Charles G. Leland quotes in his *Etruscan Roman Remains* [97] a note given him by Miss Mary Owen, of St. Joseph, Missouri, that the negroes and half-breeds in southern Missouri consider the redheaded woodpecker a great sorcerer, who can appear as either a bird or as a redman with a mantle or cloak on his arm. He is supposed to be very grateful or very vengeful as his mood requires. He sometimes bores holes in the heads of his enemies, while they sleep, and puts in maggots which keep the victims forever restless and crazy. He made the bat by putting a rat and a bird together.

CHAPTER XIII

BIRDS AND THE LIGHTNING

NOTHING in nature, except perhaps the rising and setting of the sun, has impressed mankind more than the fearsome phenomena of a thunder-storm. Such a storm in the Rocky Mountains, or among the Californian Sierras, is truly terrifying in its magnificence, and it is none the less so in the Alps or Himalayas or on the volcanic summits of Central Africa. The lightnings dart about the darkly clouded peaks, and the thunder-crashes leap from cliff to cliff in echoes that stun one, for they seem like vast iron missiles hurled by Titanic strength, and rebounding from crags that are falling in prodigious ruin—perhaps on your head.

On the plains, too, such a storm may be fearfully grand, for amid rolling thunders and a tremendous downpour of rain come an incessant flash and sparkle of lightnings that illuminate the prairie with a violet flame almost blinding in its glare. A person who did not comprehend the physical meaning of such a display might well be excused for trembling in awe and terror—moreover, the danger is real.

I believe that almost from the first there were wise men, the philosophers of their time, who understood that the clouds were fleeting masses of fog, that rain was the water pressed out of them, and that the lightning and its associated rumble were somehow as natural as the blowing of the wind. The mass of wondering and terrified people, however, could not think of the rush and noise and glare of stormy weather otherwise than as something produced by living beings of huge, mysterious and usually destructive power; and they were as real to them, although invisible, as are the electric currents and tremendous air-vibrations to us. Among the aboriginal Chinese electricity was represented as residing on the mountains in the form of birds, and their Thunder-god is pictured with a bird's beak and claws, and armed with a drum and hammer.

"The drama of mythology," De Gubernatis tells us, "has its origin in the sky; but the sky may be either clear or gloomy; it may be illumined by the sun or by the moon; it may be obscured by the darkness of night, or the condensation of its vapors into clouds. . . . The god who causes rain to fall, who from the highest heaven fertilizes the earth, takes the form now of a ram, now of a bull; the lightning that flies like a winged arrow, is represented now as a bird, now as winged horse; and thus, one after another, all the shifting phenomena of the heavens take the form of animals, becoming at length now the hero himself, now the animal that waits upon the hero, and without which he would possess no supernatural power whatever."

To the minds of the redmen in the eastern part of the United States the violent storms frequent in summer were somehow produced by vague supernatural beings spoken of as Thunder-gods; but on the open prairies and plains of the West, where even more terrific electric disturbances occur, and also along the Northwest Coast and in Alaska, they were attributed to birds of enormous size, who darkened the rain-clouds with their shadows and produced thunder by flapping their wings and lightning by opening their eyes, shooting flaming arrows, and so forth.	Some tribes believed in one such bird only, others in a family or flock of them variously colored, while still others declared that the agent was a giant who clothed himself in a huge bird-skin as a flying-dress.

If one asked what any one of these creatures was like, the answer usually was that it resembled a colossal eagle. The Comanches and Arapahoes described it to Dr. Mooney as a big bird with a brood of small ones, and said that it carried in its claws a quantity of arrows with which it strikes the victims of lightning.	This reminds us of the bird of Jove in classic fable, clutching the javelins of his master, the Thunderer; and a comic touch is that these southern Indians called the eagle stamped on our coins by their thunder-bird's name, innocently supposing that our national emblem was their "baa," the lightning-maker!

The Mandans, a Dakotan tribe, say that the thunder-bird has two toes on each foot—one before and one behind; and the Algonquian Blackfeet represent it on their medicine-lodges by simply drawing four black bird-claws on a yellow shank.	When it flies softly, as is usually its way, according to the Mandans, it is not heard by mankind, but when it flaps its wings violently a roaring noise is produced.	It breaks through the clouds to force a way for the rain, and the glance of its fiery eyes appears in the lightnings.	"We don't see the thunder-birds," a Winnebago Indian explained.	"We see their flashes only."

This terrifying creature dwelt on a remote mountain, or on some rocky elevation difficult of access, and built a nest as big as a village, surrounded by the bones and horns of the great animals on which it preyed. Every tribal district seems to have had at least one pair. The Indians about Lake Superior believed that theirs were at home on the beetling heights of that bold promontory on the northern shore of the lake long celebrated as Thunder Cape. This is, for natural reasons, a theatre of electric action, which the Chippeways accounted for by the fiction of a magic bird—quite as natural in its way as is the meteorology. At any rate the redmen feared to climb the mountain and prove their theory, for they said men had been struck by lightning there in impious attempts at investigating the bird-god—the old story of religious interference with scientific curiosity. These same people held that their thunder-bird sat on her eggs during fair weather, and hatched out her brood in the storm—which hatching *was* the storm.

"A place," says the ethnologist Mooney,[77] "known to the Sioux as Waqkina-oye, 'the Thunderer's nest'—... is in eastern South Dakota in the neighborhood of Big Stone Lake. At another place, near the summit of the Coteau des Prairies, in eastern South Dakota, a number of large round boulders are pointed out as the eggs of the thunder-bird. According to the Comanches there is a place on upper Red River where the thunder-bird once alighted on the ground. ... The same people tell how a hunter once shot and wounded a large bird which fell to the ground. Being afraid to attack it alone on account of its size, he returned to camp for help, but on again approaching the spot the hunters heard the thunder rolling and saw flashes of lightning shooting out from the ravine where the bird lay wounded. On coming nearer the lightning blinded them so that they could not see the bird, and one flash struck and killed a hunter. His frightened companions then fled back to camp, for they knew it was a thunder-bird."

In contrast to this the Eskimos of the lower Yukon Valley tell of a former man of their race who dared, after others had failed, to raid the lair of and kill a gigantic fowl that for a long time had preyed as a "man-eater" on the village of their ancestors; and they have held this man in high honor as a hero to this day.

This conception of a thunder-and-lightning-producing bird has a prominent place among the notions of the native inhabitants of the northwestern American coast-country, where the attributed characteristics and deeds vary with local surroundings and tribal peculiarities. In one place a storm was supposed to result from its activity in catching whales; and a Chehalis legend has it that Thunderbird sprang from a whale killed by South Wind. As soon as it was born South Wind followed it, and Ootz-Hooi, the giantess, found its nest and threw the eggs down a cliff. From these eggs sprang the Chehalis people. The Tlingit, of the Southern Alaskan coast-region, account for the great amount of rain that falls in a thunder-shower by explaining that the thunder-bird carries a lake on its back. A conventional representation of the thunder-bird as it appears to the Haidas of this Northwest Coast decorates the title-page of this book.

The Salish Indians of the Thomson River region, in southern British Columbia, believe that the thunder-bird uses its wings as bows to shoot arrows, i.e., lightnings. "The rebound of his wings in the air, after shooting, makes the thunder. For this reason the thunder is often heard in different parts of the sky at once, being the noise from each wing. The arrowheads fired by the thunder are found in many parts of the country. They are of black stone and of very large size." The last statement may refer to meteoric stones, or it may be purely fanciful. A common belief among the farmer-folk of Europe is that the smooth, chisel-shaped tools or weapons of prehistoric (Neolithic) men, frequently turned up by the plow, and known technically as "celts," are thunderbolts; but this is only incidental to the present theme.

The raven is a hero-bird among the Cherokees, who say that he became black by attempting to bring fire from a hollow tree that had been set on fire purposely by "the Thunderer" by means of lightning. The bird did not succeed, and blackened its plumage forever.

In Japan the ptarmigan, a dweller on mountain-tops, is called *rai-cho,* "thunder-bird," and is "sacred to the God of Thunder," as Weston expresses it, adding that "pictures of them are often hung up in farmers' cottages as a charm against lightning."

Thunderstorms are usually accompanied by much wind, and the common conception of birds as the agent of wind, or the wind itself, has been exhibited briefly in another chapter; it prevailed not only among our American Indians but in various other parts of the world, including South Africa—or did, when men were less skeptical of such ideas than now. In ancient Sanskrit mythology the delicate white cirrus cloud drifting overhead was a fleeting swan, and so also was it in the creed of the early Scandinavians and to our wild Navahoes—a good illustration not only of independent and parallel images for an idea, but of the likeness of human minds under great diversity of race and conditions.

Black clouds were thought of by the Norse folks as "ravens coursing over the earth and returning to whisper the news in the ear of listening Odin," as Baring-Gould expresses it. The immemorial resemblance traced between bird and cloud is not far-fetched: and recurs to the modern poet as it did in olden times to the Psalmist when he spoke of the wings of the wind. "The rushing vapor is the roc of the *Arabian Nights,* which broods over its great luminous egg, the sun, and which haunts the sparkling Valley of Diamonds, the starry sky. . . . If the cloud was supposed to be a great bird, the lightnings were regarded as writhing worms or serpents in its beak. . . . The lightning-bolt, shattering all it struck, was regarded as the stone dropped by the cloud-bird." [54]

In the *Kalevala* Puhuri, the North Wind, father of Pakkanen, the Frost, is sometimes personified as a gigantic eagle.

These facts and considerations prepare the way for legends that began to be told in the very beginning of things, because then, and until yesterday, all ordinary folks thought them true as well as interesting; and they are repeated even now as curiosities of primitive faith—stories of birds and plants called "openers."

The oldest, perhaps, is the Rabbinical legend of Solomon, who desired to obtain a stone-breaking "worm" (so the idea was even then ancient!) in possession of Asmodeus, the Demon of Destruction. Asmodeus refused to fetch it, and told Solomon that if he wanted this magic creature (whose name was *schamir*) he must find the nest of "the," not "a," moorhen and cover it with a plate of glass so that the motherbird could not get access to her young. This was done. When the moorhen returned and saw the situation she flew away, brought the schamir from its hiding-place, and was about to lay it on the glass, which it would break; but Benaiah, Solomon's agent, who lay in wait, shouted, and so frightened the bird that she dropped the schamir, whereupon Benaiah picked it up, as he had planned to do. It was by aid of this "worm," which shaped the stone-work for him, that Solomon was able to build his Temple without sound of hammer or saw. Other versions assert that a raven or an eagle was the bird, and that the magic glass-breaker was a stone brought from the uttermost East.

The story travelled to Greece, and there became attached to the hoopoe, a small crested bird that figures largely in south-European and African wonder-tales. A hoopoe, runs the Greek story, had a nest in an old wall in which was a crevice. The proprietor, noticing the rent in his wall, plastered it over; thus when the hoopoe returned to feed her young she found that the nest had been covered so that she was unable to enter it.

Forthwith she flew away in quest of a plant called poa (the springwort?), and having found a spray returned and applied it to the plaster, which at once fell off from the crack and gave her free access to her nest. Then she went forth to seek food, but during her absence the master again plastered up the hole. The object was again removed by means of the magic poa, and a third time the hole was stopped and opened in the same way.

The springwort and several other flowering plants were credited in old times with a magical property in opening locks. "Pliny records the superstition concerning it almost in the same form in which it is now found in Germany. If anyone touches a lock with it the lock, however strong, must yield. . . . One cannot easily find it oneself, but generally the woodpecker [according to Pliny, also the raven; in Switzerland and Swabia the hoopoe; in the Tyrol the swallow] will bring it under the following circumstances: When the bird visits its nest the nest must be stopped up with wood. The bird will open it by touching it with a spring-wurzel. Meantime a fire or a red cloth must be placed near by, which will so frighten the bird that it will let the magic root fall."

The English antiquary Aubrey (1626-97) records an anecdote of a keeper of a baronial park in Herefordshire who "did for exprinent's sake drive an iron naile thwert the hole of the woodpecker's nest, there being a tradition that the damme will bring some leafe to open it. He layed at the bottom of the tree a cleane sheet, and before many houres passed the naile came out, and he found a leafe lying by it on the sheet. They say the moonwort will do such things." The moonwort is a fern which was formerly reputed to have power to draw nails out of horseshoes.

From such roots as these grew the superstitions and legends innumerable of plants that would cure a snake (another lightning-symbol) or other animal of wounds, or even restore the dead. A tradition of the Middle Ages is that two little birds were seen fighting till one was exhausted. "It went away and ate of a certain herb and then returned to renew the battle. When the old man who witnessed the encounter had seen this done several times he took away the herb on which the bird was wont to feed, whereupon the little bird, unable to find its plant, set up a great cry and died." It is a foolish little story, but illustrative.

One reads of magic crystals, and of gems with marvellous properties that would open mountains in which princes or glittering treasures were hidden. A curious example of this is related by Leland [97] anent the constant and ordinarily fruitless hunt for treasure in ancient Etruscan tombs, which went on in Italy for centuries.

"When one would find a treasure," the peasants told Leland, "he must take the door of the house in which he
dwells and carry it forth into the fields at night until
he comes to a tree. Then he must wait till many birds
fly over him, and when they come he must throw down
the door, making a great noise. Then the birds in fear
will speak with a human voice, and tell where the treasure is buried."

Much of this tinctures the mental life of many un-
educated persons to this day. They will tell you now
at Rauen, in Germany, that a princess is entombed alive
in the Markgrafenstein, and that she and her wealth
can be released only by one who will go there on a
Friday at midnight carrying a white woodpecker—
which would seem to make an albino of that species
well worth searching for! The woodpecker of old was
a "lightning-bird" because, among other reasons, it was
supposed to get fire by boring into wood, as did primitive savages by means of the fire-drill; and its red cap
was not only a badge of its office, but a lightning-symbol
in general.

Let me illuminate this matter still more by quoting
the comments of John Fiske [98] on the mythical concep-
tions of this character that are so old, and so cherished
among the unlearned:

Among the birds enumerated by Kuhn [author of *The
Descent of Fire*] and others as representing the storm-cloud,
are likewise the wren or kinglet (French *roitelet*); the owl,
sacred to Athenæ; the cuckoo, stork and sparrow; and the
red-breasted robin, whose name Robert was originally an
epithet of the lightning-god Thor. In certain parts of France
it is still believed that the robbing of a wren's nest will render
the culprit liable to be struck by lightning. The same belief
was formerly entertained in Teutonic countries with respect
to the robin. . . .

Now, as the raven or woodpecker, in the various myths of schamir, is the dark storm-cloud, so the rock-splitting worm, or plant or pebble is nothing more or less than the flash of lightning carried and dropped by the cloud . . .

The persons who told these stories were not weaving ingenious allegories about thunder-storms, or giving utterance to superstitions of which the original meaning was forgotten. The old grannies who, along with a stoical indifference to the fate of quails and partridges, used to impress upon me the wickedness of killing robins, did not add that I should be struck by lightning if I failed to heed their admonitions. They had never heard that the robin was the bird of Thor: they merely rehearsed the remnant of the superstition which had survived to their own times, while the essential part of it had long since faded from recollection. The reason for regarding a robin's life as more sacred than a partridge's had been forgotten; but it left behind, as was natural, a vague recognition of that mythical sanctity. The primitive meaning of a myth fades away as inevitably as the primitive meaning of a word or phrase; and the rabbins which told of a worm which shattered rocks no more thought of the writhing thunderbolts than the modern reader thinks of oyster-shells when he sees the word *ostracism,* or consciously breathes a prayer when he writes the phrase *Good-bye.*

CHAPTER XIV

LEGENDS IN A HISTORICAL SETTING

IT is not easy in preparing a book devoted mainly to fable and folklore to sort out material for a separate chapter on "legends." A legend may be defined as a narrative of something thought of as having actually happened in connection with some real purpose or place, but which is unsupported by historical evidence. In many cases such narratives are quite incredible, but even so they may have a historically illustrative, a literary, or at least an amusing interest. Stories of a considerable number of well-known kinds of birds are in this way connected with actual persons, or with verifiable incidents of the past, and hence may be said to be "legends in an historical setting." A fair example of them is the incident of the Capitoline geese.

Early in the third century before the Christian era a horde of Gaulish invaders under Brennus over-ran central Italy, and in 388 B. C. captured all of Rome itself except the lofty citadel called the Capitol, where a Roman general officer, Marcus Manlius, held out with a small garrison on the point of starvation. One night the besieging Gauls, having discovered an unguarded by-path, crept up the rocky steep, intending the surprise and capture of the almost worn-out defenders. "But," says Plutarch,[94] in Dryden's translation, "there were sacred Geese kept near the Temple of Juno, which at other times were plentifully fed, but at this time, by

reason of the Corn and all other Provisions were grown
strait, their allowance was shorten'd and they themselves
in a poor and lean condition. This Creature is by nature
of quick sense, and apprehensive of the least noise; so
that besides watchful through hunger, and restless, they
immediately discovered the coming of the Gauls; so that
running up and down, with their noise and cackling they
raised the whole camp."

Manlius sprang from sleep, aroused a body of soldiers
and repelled the attack. It was the beginning of an
ultimate victory over the enemy. Rome was saved,
and in recognition of it Manilus was given the honorary
title Capitolinus, and for a long time afterward the
incident was celebrated annually by a procession to the
Capitol in which a golden goose was carried. Livy also
tells us in his history that the prototype of this golden
symbol was a single sentinel goose never seen before,
hence a divine aid sent to Rome for the purpose by the
gods. It is interesting to note that

> These consecrated geese in orders
> That to the capitol were warders
> And being then upon patrol
> With noise alone beat off the Gaul,

as *Hudibras* has it, were "sacred" to Juno, for this was
before the time when she, having changed from the
status of simple wife to Jupiter (and a model to human
wives), had become the imperious and trouble-making
empress of later days, and had discarded the motherly
goose for the exotic, proud, and royally splendid peacock. This is a capital example of the adaptive character of the assignment of birds to the various demigods
of the Roman pantheon; and it suggests the query

whether in some principal cases reverence for the bird itself did not precede the conception of the divinity it afterward typified.

Another tale of birds acting as sentinels explains how the wren came to be so mortally hated by the Irish, whose cruel "hunting of the wren" is described in another chapter. According to Lady Wilde,[60] a student of Irish folklore, this hatred is owing to the fact that once when Irish troops were approaching to attack a part of Thomas Cromwell's army (about 1650) "wrens came and perched on the Irish drums, and by their tapping and noise aroused the English soldiers, who fell on the Irish troops and killed all of them." This is a variant of a legend far older than Cromwell's campaigning; and it is not the true explanation of the antipathy the cruder Irish and Manxmen still feel toward this innocent little songster, while at the same time they have a peculiar tenderness for the robin.

A third parallel is found in the annoyance caused the Scottish Covenanters. Many a meeting of pious Presbyterians in some hidden, heathery glen of the misty hills was discovered and roughly dispersed "because of the hovering, bewailing plovers, fearful for their young, clamoring overhead." The poet Leyden alludes to the long-remembered grudge against this suspicious bird when, speaking of the religious refugees on the moors, he writes:

> The lapwing's clamorous whoop attends their flight,
> Pursues their steps where'er the wanderers go,
> Till the shrill scream betrays them to the foe.

Returning to ancient history, two bird-stories of Alexander the Great are delightful as illustrating how

an independent and masterful intellect, even in that early
day above the Pagan superstitions of the time, might
with ingenuity and boldness bend the sanctions of
religion to his own ends without destroying them. The
first one is an incident recorded of Alexander's campaign in Asia Minor in 334 B. C. His fleet was an-
chored in the harbor of Miletus, and opposite it lay the
fleet of the Persians. Alexander had no desire to disturb
this situation, for he meant his army, not the navy,
to do the work in view. One day an eagle, Jove's
bird, was seen sitting on the shore behind the Macedonian ships, and Parmenion, chief of staff, found in
this fact convincing indication by the gods that victory
was with the ships. Alexander pointed out that the
eagle had perched on the land, not on the ships, giving
thereby the evident intimation that it was only through
the victory of the troops on land that the fleet could have
value. As Alexander was commander-in-chief, this was
evidently the orthodox interpretation.

Two years later Alexander was one day laying out
on its site the plan of his foreordained city of Alex-
andria, in Egypt, and was marking the course of the
proposed streets by sprinkling lines of flour in the lack
of chalk-dust. "While the king," says Plutarch, "was
congratulating himself on his plan, on a sudden a countless number of birds of various sorts flew over from
the land and the lake in clouds, and settling on the spot
in clouds devoured in a short time all the flour, so that
Alexander was much disturbed in mind at the omen
involved, till the augurs restored his confidence, telling
him the city . . . was destined to be rich in its resources,
and a feeder of nations of men."

The straight face with which Plutarch [94] recites these

and similar stories of hocus-pocus in the matter of inconvenient omens is delightful; but the faith of the common people was not so easily shaken. For example: When the Sicilian-Greek army of Agathocles, Tyrant of Syracuse in the third century, B. C., was facing near Times a more powerful Carthaginian force, Agathocles let loose a number of owls among his men, "who suddenly took great courage as the birds sacred to Pallas settled blinking upon their helmets and shields"—and they routed the bigger enemy. That was true religious inspiration—as true as ever blazed in the heart of Christian crusader; but it was a sacrilegous trick on the part of Agathocles!

Just across the strait from Sicily, at Regium (Reggio), was the home of the celebrated cranes of Ibycus. Ibycus, a local poet, was being murdered by robbers when he called on the cranes fluttering near by to give witness of his death. Later, the murderers were one day at the theatre, when they saw a flock of cranes, and in fright whispered to one another: "The cranes of Ibycus!" They were overheard, arrested and executed, whence the proverb "the cranes of Ibycus" to express crime coming unexpectedly to light.

The Wonderful Magazine, an amazing periodical issued in London from 1793 to 1798, contained a story that in 1422 a "Roman" emperor besieging Zeta took all the sparrows his men could catch, and, tying lighted matches to their feet, let them go toward the town. But the citizens made a great noise, and the frightened sparrows flying back set the Roman camp on fire and so raised the siege. The reader may put his own estimate on this bit of historical lore; and may discover, if he can, where and what was Zeta.

Arabs in Palestine tell how a bird was involved in
David's sin of coveting Uriah's wife. David, they say,
had shut himself up in a tower for meditation, when,
happening to look up, he saw just outside the window
a bird of amazing beauty—a pigeon whose plumage
gleamed like gold and jewels. David threw some
crumbs on the floor, whereupon the pigeon came in and
picked them up, but eluded David's attempt to capture
it. At last, to escape his efforts, it flew to the window
and settled on one of the bars. He pursued, but it
departed. It was then, as David followed the bright
creature with longing eyes, that he caught sight of
Madame Uriah in the bath—and was done for!

Among other excellent things in Hanauer's *Tales
from Palestine* [43] is the following report of Solomon's
contest with a dove:

"In the southern wall of the Kubbet 'es-Sakhra [at
Jerusalem], the mosque that now stands near the site
of the ancient Temple, on the right side of the door as
one enters there is a gray slab framed in marble of a
dark color. It contains a figure, formed by natural
veins in the stone, which is distinct enough to be taken
for a picture of two doves perched facing each other on
the edge of a vase. With this picture is connected a
tale . . .

"The great king Solomon understood the language
of beasts, birds and fishes, and, when he had occasion
to do so, would converse with all of them. One day,
soon after he had completed the Temple, as he was
standing at a window of the royal palace, he overheard
a conversation between a pair of birds that were sitting on the housetop. Presently the male, who was
evidently trying to impress the female with his im-

portance, exclaimed: 'Solomon is a conceited fool! Why
should he be so vain of this pile of buildings he has
raised? I, if I wished, could kick them all over in a
few minutes.'

"The king, greatly enraged by this pompous speech,
summoned the offender into his presence and demanded
what he meant by such an outrageous boast. 'Your
majesty,' replied the bird, 'will, I am sure, forgive my
audacity, when I explain that I was in the company
of a female; since your majesty doubtless knows from
experience that in such circumstances the temptation to
boast is almost irresistible.' The monarch, forgetting
his anger in his amusement, said with a smile: 'Go your
way this time, but see that you do not repeat the offence,'
and the bird, after a profound obeisance, flew away to
rejoin his mate.

"He had hardly alighted before the female, unable to
repress her curiosity, eagerly inquired why he had been
summoned to the palace. 'Oh,' said the impudent
boaster, 'the king heard me tell you that if I chose I
could kick down all his buildings in no time, and he
sent for me to beg me not to do it.'

"Solomon, who, of course, heard this remark also, was
so indignant at the incorrigible vanity of its author that
he at once turned both birds into stone. They remain
to this day as a reminder of the saying: 'The peace of
mankind consists in guarding the tongue.' "

But the stories of Solomon and his bird-friends are
many. He was evidently a jolly old soul, and tradition
says that when he travelled across the desert clouds of
birds formed a canopy to protect him from the sun.
The hoopoe, a high-crested bird that figures largely in
other fanciful tales of the East, tells wise Solomonic

stories, and is still regarded by Saharan nomads as possessed of peculiar virtues. The great Jewish king, whose reality is almost hidden under the legendary mantle, is said to have chosen the hoopoe, the cock and the pewit: the first because of its wit, the second in admiration of its cry, and the third because, says Hanauer, it can see through the earth, and could tell him where fountains of water could be found. The last preference is natural in an arid region, the pewit being a water-bird, the familiar lapwing-plover; and as it annually migrates through Palestine into Ethiopia it is reasonable that it should be fabled to be the means of bringing Solomon and the Queen of Sheba together, as is described in Chapter XXVII of the Koran. It should be noted that all of these birds are crested.

The veneration given to doves by the Mohammedans at Mecca is accounted for elsewhere; but swallows are held in almost equal reverence by both officials and pilgrims at that great shrine of Islam, and build their nests in the haram. This respect is explained by Keane [14] as the result of a belief that they were the instruments by which Mecca was saved from the Abyssinian (Christian) army that is known to have invaded Arabia in the year of Mohammed's birth, and to have been disastrously expelled. The tradition is that God sent flocks of swallows, every bird carrying three small stones in its beak and two in its claws, which were dropped on the heads of the Abyssinians, and miraculously penetrated the bodies of men and elephants until only one of the invaders was left alive. He fled back to his country, and had just finished telling of the disaster to the king when one of the swallows, which had followed him from Mecca, dropped its pebble and killed

him too. The kernel of this dramatic story is in the
nineteenth section of the Koran: [59] "And he sent against
them birds in flocks (ababils), claystones did he hurl
down at them." The historical explanation is that the
Abyssinian invaders were destroyed by small-pox, the
pustules of which are called in Arabic by a word meaning "small stones."

Of a piece with these traditions and the Rabbinical
tales of the Jews are the monkish legends preserved in
early British chronicles, such as that by the Venerable
Bede or by William of Malmesbury. The orthodox as
well as dissenters had trouble with birds. Among the
traditions of the celebrated Scotch-Irish missionary
Columba (Latinized from his baptismal name Colum,
"dove") is one that once in his ardent youth Colum was
trying to make by stealth in a church a copy of the
psalter in possession of the selfish king, Finian of Done-
gal, who had refused the young enthusiast that privilege.
A meddlesome stork, confined within the church, informed the sacristan, and Colum was arrested. Nevertheless by divine aid he got his copy, helpful to him
afterward in his beneficent work in the Scottish highlands.

One of the prettiest of these old stories is that of
St. Kenneth and the gulls.[22] One day about A. D. 550
the blackheaded gulls, flying as usual along the coast of
Wales, and scanning the sea sharply for food or anything else interesting to a gull, found floating in a
coracle—a round, wickerwork canoe—a human baby a
day or two old, contentedly asleep on a pallet made of
a folded purple cloth. Several gulls seized the corners
of this cloth and so carried the child to the ledge of
the Welsh cliff where they nested, plucked feathers from

their breasts to make a soft bed, laid the baby on it, then hastened to fly inland and bring a doe to provide it with milk, for which an angel offered a brazen bell as a cup. There the blessed waif lived for several months; but one day, in the absence of all the gulls, a shepherd discovered the infant and took him down to his hut and his kind wife. The gulls, returning from the sea, heard of this act from the doe. They at once rushed to the shepherd's cottage, again lifted the babe by the corners of its purple blanket, and bore him back to the ledge of their sea-fronting crag. There he stayed until he had grown to manhood—a man full of laughter and singing and kind words; and the Welsh peasants of the Gower Peninsula revered him and called him Saint Kenneth.

Somewhat similar is the legendary history of Coemagen, or Saint Kelvin, an Irish monk of the eighth century, into whose charge was committed the infant son of Colman, a Leinster noble. "Coemagen fed the child on the milk of a doe which came from the forest to the door of his cell. A raven was wont, after the doe had been milked, to perch on the bowl, and sometimes would upset it. 'Bad luck to thee!' exclaimed the saint. 'When I am dead there will be a famous wake, but no scraps for thee and thy clan!' When very old St. Kelvin moved into a forest hermitage, where the birds came to him as companions. Once, while praying, his supplicating palms outstretched, a blackbird (thrush) dropped her eggs into the hollow of his hands, and he held his arms rigid until the chicks hatched."

A curious parallel to the last incident is quoted by the Baroness Martinengo-Caesaresco [20] "from an industrious translator" of the book *Tatchi-Lou-Lun,* describing how

when a bird laid her eggs on the head of the first
Buddha, which she mistook for the branch of a tree,
he plunged himself into a trance so as not to move
until the eggs had hatched and the young were flown.

St. Bede the younger, a contemporary of Coemagen,
had a dove that used to come at his call; and an Irish
monk, Comgall, would bid the swans near his residence
come and cluster devotionally around his feet. Many
saints, the legends declare, had authority over birds,
and one, St. Millburg, abbess of Wenlock, in Shropshire, kept them out of the farmers' crops by telling
them it was naughty to despoil the grain. Of old, according to Canon Kingsley, St. Guthlac in Crowland
said, as the swallows sat upon his knee, "He who leads
his life according to the will of God, to him will the
wild deer and the wild birds draw more near."

The religious "hermits," so prevalent at that period,
were men who chose a more or less solitary life, quite
as much, I suspect, on account of their love of nature
as from purely devotional motives, and this was particularly true of those in Great Britain, exhibiting the
characteristic British fondness for animal life. There
was an early St. Bartholomew, for example, who in the
sixth century or thereabout dwelt in seclusion on one
of the Farne Islands off the northeastern coast of England, and made friends of the gulls and cormorants of
the place. One of these he had tamed to eat out of his
hand, and once, when Bartholomew was away fishing,
a hawk pursued this poor bird into the chapel and killed
it. Brother Bartholomew came in and found the hawk
there with bloody talons and a shame-faced appearance.
He caught it, kept it two days without food to punish
it, then let it go. At another time, as he sat by the

shore, a cormorant approached and pulled at his skirt, then led him to where one of its young had fallen into a crevice of the rocks whence the good man rescued it.

One of these rocky islets in the North Sea became so famous during the next century that it has been known ever since as Holy Isle, and the ruins of its monastery and cathedral still remain and may be seen from the railway train as it passes along the brink of the lofty coast a little south of Berwick-on-Tweed. This was the seat of the renowned Bishop Cuthbert of whom many quaint stories are told, apart from the record of his religious work. They attribute to his influence the extraordinary gentleness and familiarity characteristic of the eider duck, which is known to this day in Northumbria as Cuthbert's bird. It was he, according to a narrative of a monk of the 13th century, who inspired these ducks with a hereditary trust in mankind by taking them as companions of his solitude when for several years he resided alone on Lindisfarne. There is good reason to accept this and similar traditions as largely true, for a like ability in "gentling" birds and other wild animals is manifested today by some persons of a calm and kindly sort.

Early in the eighth century a monk of intensely ascetic disposition, named Guthlac, retired to a solitary hermitage on an island in the dismal morasses of Lincolnshire, which afterward, if not then, was called Croyland or Crowland. He was sorely tempted by the Devil we are informed, and had many battles with "demons" —native British refugees hiding in the fens; but in the intervals of his fasting and fighting he got acquainted with the wild creatures about him. "The ravens, the beasts and the fishes," says the record, "came to obey him. Once a venerable brother named Wilfred visited him, and . . . suddenly two swallows came flying in . . . and often they sat fearlessly on the shoulders of the holy man Guthlac, and then lifted up their song, and afterward they sat on his bosom and on his arms and his knees. . . . When Guthlac died angelic songs were heard in the sky, and all the air had a wondrous odor of exceeding sweetness."

St. Kentigern, when a schoolboy, was wrongly accused of having twisted off the head of his master's pet robin. He proved his innocence by putting the head and body together, whereupon the robin came to life and attended Kentigern until he became a great and good man. His master was St. Servan, and the robin was one that used to eat from his hand and perch on his shoulder, where it would twitter whenever Servan chanted the Psalms.

Here we encounter the mystical kind of story with which those old chroniclers like to embellish their biographies of holy men, and there was no limit to their credulity. Such is the tale of Carilef, a French would-be hermit of Ménàt, in Auvergne, who thought he was guided to set up a religious station because a wren had laid an egg in a hood that he had left hanging on a bush—a very wrenlike proceeding; and that was the foundation of the monastery about which the city of St. Calais grew in later times. Several other incidents of this kind are on record, showing that the value placed on any action by a bird that could be construed as a divine message. It is written that Editha, one of the early queens of England, persuaded her husband to found a religious house near Oxford on account of the omens she interpreted from the voice and actions of a

certain magpie. Similarly the site for the abbey of
Thierry, near Rheims, in France, was indicated to St.
Theodoric, in the sixth century, by a white eagle circling around the top of the hill on which it subsequently
was erected; and this miraculous eagle was seen year
after year in the sky above it.

About that time Kenelm, son and heir of Kenulph,
king of Wessex, was seven years old. His sister, who
wanted to succeed to the throne in his place, procured
his murder. The instant this was accomplished the fact
was notified to the Pope, according to the *Chronicles*
of Roger de Wendover, by a white dove that alighted
on the altar of St. Peter's, bearing in its beak a scroll
on which was written

> In Clent cow-pasture, under a thorn,
> Of head bereft lies Kenelm, king-born.

The Pope sent word to England, the body was found in
a thicket over which hung a pillar of supernal light, and
was taken to Winchelcumb, in Gloucestershire, for
burial; and at the spot near Halesowen, in Shropshire,
where he was killed, Kenelm's Chapel was erected.

But the most mystical legend in which birds are a
part, is one familiar in Brittany. It is related of St.
Leonore, a Welsh missionary who went to Brittany in
the sixth century, to whom many fabulous powers and
deeds are attributed, the most comprehensible of which
Baring-Gould has put into verse. Leonore, with a band
of followers, had decided to settle in Brittany on a
desolate moor; but they had forgotten to bring any
seed-wheat, and were alarmed.

Said the abbot, "God will help us
In this hour of bitter loss."
Then one spied a little redbreast
Sitting on a wayside cross.

Doubtless came the bird in answer
To the words the monk did speak,
For a heavy wheat-ear dangled
From the robin's polished beak.

Then the brothers, as he dropped it
Picked it up and careful sowed;
And abundantly in autumn
Reaped the harvest where they strewed.[21]

Greater poets than Baring-Gould or even Bishop
Trench have found literary material in these monastic
tales. Witness Longfellow's *Golden Legend,* where he
sings of good St. Felix, the Burgundian missionary who
crossed the Channel, and in A. D. 604 converted to
Christianity the wild king of the East Saxons; and who
listened to the singing of a milk-white bird for a hundred years, although it had seemed to him but an hour,
so enchanted was he with the music. No doubt myth-
mongers might discourse very scientifically on this and
some other of these episodes in the penumbra of history, but we will leave the pleasure of it to them.

None of these traditions of early bird-lovers and
teachers of kindness are so pleasant as are those inspired
by the gracious life of St. Francis.[22] A familiar classic
is his sermon to the birds when

Around Assisi's convent gate
The birds, God's poor who cannot wait,
From moor and mere and darksome wood
Came flocking for their dole of food.

One of the prettiest Franciscan stories is that of the saint and the nightingale as presented by Mrs. Jamieson;[105] and, by the way, antiphonal singing with birds is related of several holy men and women of old:

> As he was sitting with his disciple Leo, he felt himself penetrated with joy and consolation by the song of the nightingale . . . and Francis began to sing, and when he stopped the nightingale took up the strain; and thus they sang alternately until the night was far advanced and Francis was obliged to stop for his voice failed. Then he confessed that the little bird had vanquished him. He called it to him, thanked it for its song, and gave it the remainder of his bread; and having bestowed his blessing upon it the creature flew away.

Longfellow has preserved in melodious verse that legend of the Spanish Charles V and the swallow that chose his tent as a site for its nest at a time when the emperor—

> I forget in what campaign,
> Long besieged in mud and rain
> Some old frontier town of Flanders.
>
> Yes, it was a swallow's nest,
>   Built of clay and hair of horse's
> Mane, or tail, or dragoon's crest,
> Found on hedgerows east and west
>   After skirmish of the forces.

The headquarters staff were scandalized by the bird's impudence, but Charles forbade their malice:

> "Let no hand the bird molest,"
>   Said he solemnly, "nor hurt her!"
> Adding then, by way of jest,
>   "Golondrina is my guest,
>   'Tis the wife, of some deserter!"

So unharmed and unafraid
  Sat the swallow still and brooded,
Till the constant cannonade
Through the walls a breach had made,
  And the siege was thus concluded.

Then the army elsewhere bent
  Struck the tents as if disbanding,
Only not the Emperor's tent.
For he ordered as he went,
  Very curtly, "Leave it standing."

So it stood there all alone,
  Loosely flapping, torn and tattered,
Till the brood was fledged and flown,
Swinging o'er those walks of stone
  Which the cannon-shot had shattered.

CHAPTER XV

SOME PRETTY INDIAN STORIES

N OT many of the stories about birds now or formerly current among the American aborigines
are of a pleasing character. They are fantastic
myths for the most part, as appears from many of the
incidents given elsewhere in this book; and often they
are so wildly improbable, incoherent, and unbirdlike as
to disgust rather than interest us. That is partly owing,
no doubt, to our difficulty in taking the native point of
view, and our ignorance of the significance the half-
animal, half-human characters in the tales have to the
redmen, with whom, in most cases, the startling narratives pass for veritable tribal history. Their stories are
as foreign to our minds as is their "tum-tum" music
to our ears. Now and then, however, we come across
an understanding and pleasing legend, of purely native
origin, and touched with poetic feeling.

A favorite story among the central Eskimos, for instance, is that of their race-mother Sedna, who was the
daughter of a chief, and was wooed by a fulmar (a
kind of northern petrel) who promised her, if she would
marry him, a delightful life in his distant home. So
she went away with him. But she had been ruefully
deceived, and was cruelly mistreated. A year later her
father went to pay her a visit; and discovering her
misery he killed her husband and took his repentant
daughter home. The other fulmars in the village fol-

lowed them, mourning and crying for their murdered
fellow, and fulmars continue to utter doleful cries to
this day.

Another Eskimo tale relates that a loon told a poor
blind boy that he could cure him of his affliction. So
the boy crept after the bird to a lake, where the loon
took him and dived with him into the water. Three
times they repeated their submergence, the last time
staying a long time under the water, but when the boy
came to the surface after the third diving he had good
eyesight. This seems one of the rare examples of a
tale told simply for its own sake, and free of any esoteric significance.

A very pretty legend, current among the Eskimos of
western Alaska, has been preserved for us by Edward
W. Nelson,[101] who spent several years, late in the
19th century, in studying the ornithology and ethnology of the Bering Sea region. It relates to the redpolls, the most abundant and entertaining land-birds of
Alaska, where it would be a surprisingly hard heart that
was not touched by their companionship as winter closes
down on a dreary landscape of snow-drifts. Let me
quote Mr. Nelson's words:

At this season the stars seem each to hang from the firmament by an invisible cord, and twinkle clear and bright overhead. The sharp, querulous yelp of the white fox alone breaks
the intense stillness. A white, frosty fog hangs in the air—
the chilled breath of nature—which falls silently to the ground
in the lovely crystal handiwork of northern genii. In the
north a pale auroral arch moves its mysterious banners, and
the rounding bosom of the earth, chill under its white mantle,
looks dreary and sad. After such a night the sun seems to
creep reluctantly above the horizon, as though loath to face
the bitter cold. The smoke rises slowly and heavily in the
fixed atmosphere, and warm rooms are doubly appreciated.

Soon small troops of these little redpolls come . . . flitting
about the houses on all sides, examining the bare spots on the
ground, searching the old weeds and fences, clinging to the
eaves, and even coming to the window-sills, whence they peer
saucily in, making themselves continually at home, and re-
ceiving a hearty welcome for their cheering presence. The
breast is now a beautiful peach-blossom pink, and the crown
shining scarlet. How this bird came to bear these beautiful
colors is told in one of the Indian myths . . . which begins
thus:

Very long ago the whole of mankind was living in cheer-
less obscurity. Endless night hid the face of the world, and
men were without the power of making a fire, as all the fire
of the world was in the possession of a ferocious bear living
in a far-off country to the north. The bear guarded his charge
with unceasing vigilance, and so frightful was his appearance
that no man dared attempt to obtain any of the precious substance. While the poor Indians were sorrowing over their
misfortunes the redpoll, which at that time was a plain little
wood-sparrow, dressed in ordinary dull brown, heard their
plaint—for in those days men and beasts understood one
another,—and his heart was touched. He prepared himself
for a long journey and set out toward the lodge of the cruel
bear. After many adventures . . . he reached the place, and
by a successful ruse stole a living ember from the perpetual
fire which glowed close under the breast of the savage guar-
dian, and flew away back with it in his beak. The glow of
the coal was reflected from his breast and crown, while his
forehead became slightly burned. Far away he flew, and
finally arrived safely at the home of mankind, and was received with great rejoicing.

He gave the fire to the grateful people and told them to
guard it well; and as he did so they noticed the rich glow on
his breast and brow, and said: "Kind bird, wear forever that
beautiful mark as a memento of what you have done for us;"
and to this day the redpoll wears this badge in proof of the
legend, as all may see, and mankind has ever since had fire.

One might gather a considerable collection of historical anecdotes relating to birds that in one way or
another aided the Indians of old to obtain or to preserve
fire, and some of them are noted incidentally elsewhere

in this volume; but few are as poetic and entertaining
as Mr. Nelson's contribution.

The late Charles G. Leland found among the Algonkins of Maine and eastward a great number of tales
that he put into his books. One or two of them are
about birds, and these he threw into verse and published them in a volume entitled *Kuloskap the Master*.[91]
The longest and most romantic of these is the love-
story of the Leaf for the Red Bird (scarlet tanager),
quoted in part below:

> In the earliest time on the greatest mountain
> Lived merry Mipis, the little leaf . . .
> Listens all day to the birds and the breezes,
> And goes to sleep to the song of the owl.
>
> Merry Mipis on a bright May morning
> Was stretching himself in the warm sunshine
> When he heard afar a wonderful music,
> A sound like a flute and the voice of a maiden,
> Rippling melodies melting in one.
> Never before had he heard such singing.
> Then looking up he beheld before him
> A beautiful merry little bird-girl,
> Dressed in garments of brilliant scarlet,
> Just like his own in the Indian summer.
> "O fairest of small birds," said merry Mipis,
> "Who are you, and what is your name?"
> Thus she answered: "I am Squ'tes,
> The Little Fire. . . .
> I have lived in the deep green forest,
> Even as you have for many ages,
> Singing my songs to K'musom'n,
> Unto our Father the mighty mountain;
> And, because he well loved my music,
> For a reward he sent me hither
> To seek a youth whose name is Mipis,
> Whom he wills that I should wed."

This unexpected and rather unmaidenly avowal rather

startled Mipis, and made him suspicious of some trick-
ery, despite the attraction of her charm; but Squ'tes,
"never heeding what the leaf thought," began again—

> Pouring out in the pleasant sunshine
> Her morning song. As Mipis listened
> To the melodious trill he melted;
> For the sweet tune filled all the forest,
> Every leaf on the tree was listening. . . .
> And as the music grew tender and stronger,
> And as in one long soft note it ended,
> Little Leaf said to her: "Be my own."
> So in the greenwood they lived together.

One day both go to the Mountain and thank him for
their happiness; and in the course of the visit the grandsire warns them not to go away from the Mountain,
for dangers fill the outside world, thus:

> The little Indian boy Monimquess,
> Who, armed with a terrible bow and arrows,
> Shoots all of the little birds of the forest;

and—

> Aplasemwesit, the Little Whirlwind,
> Who never rests. He is always trying
> To blow the leaves away from the branches.

So they built their nest on the great tree that grew
"in the safest place in all the mountain," and for a time
continued in bliss; but Mipis could see from their lofty
home a far, beautiful country, and wanted to visit it.
So Red Bird took the discontented Little Leaf in her bill
and bore him away into the delightful lowland, where
again they built a home; but here the Indian boy heard
the wonderful singing, and shot the singer, and Little
Whirlwind seized Mipis and took him to his grandsire,
the Storm, who resolved to keep Mipis as a prisoner.

That night the Mountain dreamed of this, and sent his son to demand Mipis, and the Storm gave him up, so that soon Little Leaf was back on his safe mountain-tree—but he lived in lonely grief.

> His life was gone with the Little Fire,
> And the fire of his life was all in ashes.

How then had it fared with the lost Red Bird? When she fell under the boy's arrow she was not killed but sorely wounded; and when the young Indian carried her home, very proud of his prize, his grandsire said truly that the bird must be kept captive. Red Bird recovered rapidly, and one morning Monimquess was dismayed to hear her singing as loudly as possible, "like a brook to sunshine," as he thought, for he knew she was trying to make herself heard by the Mountain, and that if she succeeded destruction would be hurled upon the wigwam. At last, wearied with anxious thinking—

> Down by the fire he lay on a bearskin
> Smoking himself into silent sleep.
> The door was closed, nor was there a crevice
> Through which the Red Bird could creep to freedom,
> When all at once she thought of the opening
> Through which the smoke from the fire ascended,
> Ever upward so densely pouring
> Nobody dreamed she would dare to pass it.
>
> As the head of Monimquess drooped on his shoulder. . . .
> Softly the Red Bird rose, and taking
> A birchen bucket filled it with water.
> Dipping her wing in the water she sprayed it
> Little by little upon the fire.
> Little by little the fire, like Monimquess,
> Sank to sleep, and the bright red flame
> Lay down to rest in the dull gray ashes.
> Out of the smoke-hole, in careful silence,
> Flitted Squ'tes. . . .

So the lovers were reunited. Then

> . . . Squ'tes and Mipis
> Lived all the summer upon the mountain,
> Sung in its shadows and shone in the sunshine.
> Still as of yore they are singing and shining;
> And so it will be while the mountain is there.

A very curious feature of this delicate romance, which reminds one of the love-story of the Nightingale and the Rose, is the transposition of sex. To our minds it would seem natural that the bird, as the most active of the two characters, should take the male part and the leaf the other; and it is false to fact that Red Bird, as a female, should *sing*. The Indians must have known that this was unnatural, yet their poetic sense arranged it otherwise, just as the poets have pictured the nightingale pressing *her* breast against a thorn, yet singing, as only male birds do!

Elsewhere I have shown how important a part the loon plays in the mythology and fireside tales of the redmen of the Northeastern region of our country and that of the Great Lakes. To the Algonkins of Maine and eastward this bird was the messenger of their great hero Glooscap, or Kuloskap, as Leland spells it with careful accuracy when writing in the language of the Pasamaquoddies; and he has told in verse the story of how this service was accepted by the willing bird. One day when Kuloskap was pursuing the gigantic magician, Winpe, his enemy, a flock of loons came circling near him, and to his question to their leader: "What is thy will, O Kwimu?" the loon replied: "I fain would be thy servant, thy servant and thy friend." Then the Master taught the loons a cry, a strange, prolonged cry, like the howl of a dog when he calls to the moon, or

when, far away in the forest, he seeks to find his master;
and he instructed them to utter this weird summons
whenever they required him.

Now it came to pass long after, the Master in Uktakumkuk
(The which is Newfoundland) came to an Indian village,
And all who dwelt therein were Kwimuuk, who had been
Loons in the time before. And now they were very glad
As men to see once more the Master, who had blessed them
When they were only birds. Therefore he made them his
    huntsmen.
Also his messengers. Hence comes that in all the stories
Which are told of the mighty Master the loons are ever his
    friends;
And the Indians, when they hear the cry of the loons, exclaim:
"Kimu elkomtuejul Kuloskapul"—the Loon is calling
Kuloskap, the Master.

Leith Adams [103] says: "Stories are told"—among the
Micmacs in New Brunswick—"how the snowy owl still
laments the Golden Age when man and all animals lived
in perfect amity until it came to pass that they began
to quarrel; when the great Glooscap, or Gotescarp, got
disgusted and sailed across the seas to return when
they made up their differences. So every night the owl
repeats to this day his *Koo, koo, skoos.* 'Oh, I am sorry,
Oh, I am sorry.' "

A quaint little legend comes from the Tillamooks,
whose home was formerly on the Oregon coast, where
the tides do not rise very much. In the beginning of
the world, it teaches, the crow had a voice like that of
the thunder-bird, and the thunder-bird the voice of a
crow. The latter proposed to exchange voices. The
crow agreed to this, but demanded that in return the
thunder-bird give her low water along the seashore,
so that she might more easily gather the clams and other
mussels, which was a part of a Tillamook woman's daily

task. The thunder-bird therefore made the water draw back a very long distance. But when the crow went out on the waste of sea-bottom she saw so many marine monsters that she was frightened, and begged the thunder-bird not to make the waters recede so far; and that is the reason that now but little ocean-bottom is exposed at ebb tide on the Oregon coast.

The Gualala Indians were a tribe of the great Pomo family that half a century ago dwelt happily in the northwestern corner of Sonoma County, California, and their staple food was the flour of crushed and filtered acorns of several kinds of oaks. In their country, as elsewhere in that State, the California woodpecker (*Melanerpes*) is a very common bird, which has the habit of drilling numerous small holes in pines and other soft-wooded trees, and fixing in each an acorn— a method of storing its favorite food against a time of famine. The Indians understood this very well, and in times of scarcity of food in camp they would cut down the small trees and climb the big ones, and rob the cupboards of the far more provident birds. "And here," says Powers,[19] "I will make mention of a kind of sylvan barometer. . . . These acorns are stored away before the rainy season sets in, sometimes to the amount of a half-bushel, and when they are wetted they presently swell and start out a little. So always, when a rainstorm is brewing, the woodpeckers fall to work with great industry a day or two in advance and hammer them in all tight. During the winter, therefore, whenever the woods are heard rattling with the pecking of these busy little commissary-clerks heading up their barrels of worms, the Indian knows a rainstorm is certain to follow."

The Chippeway Indians, as Schoolcraft noted, account for the friendly spirit of the robin by relating that he was once a young brave whose father set him a task too cruel for his strength, and made him starve too long when he had reached man's estate and had to go through the customary initiation-ceremonies. He turned into a robin, and said to his father: "I shall always be the friend of man and keep near their dwellings. I could not gratify your pride as a warrior, but I will cheer you by songs."

This pretty fiction is noteworthy, when one recalls the many instances in Greek and European myths and poetry of men and women transforming themselves into birds.

The Cherokees had an interesting story about the wren, always a busybody. She gets up early in the morning, they say, pries into everything, and goes around to every lodge in the settlement to get news for the birds' council. When a new baby is born she finds out whether it is a boy or a girl, and reports to the council. If it is a boy the birds sing in mournful chorus: "Alas! The whistle of the arrow! My shins will burn," for the birds know that when the boy grows older he will hunt them with his blowgun and arrows, and roast them on a stick. But if the baby is a girl they are glad, and sing: "Thanks! The sound of the pestle! At her home I shall surely be able to scratch where she sweeps," because they know that after a while they will be able to pick up stray grains where she beats the corn into meal.[104]

In the myths or folklore of the Pawnees a character in several tales, as related by Grinnell,[105] is a little bird, smaller than a pigeon. "Its back is blue, but its breast white, and its head is spotted. It flies swiftly over the water, and when it sees a fish it dives down into the water to catch it. This bird is a servant or a messenger for the Nahurac." The Nahurac are an assemblage of imaginary animals by whom many wonderful things are done; and it communicates to living men their wishes or orders, and acts as a guide when men are summoned to come or go somewhere. But this is perilously near the purely mythical, and it is mentioned only as an example of the widespread conception of birds as messengers and interpreters.

I hope I may be pardoned if I add to this group of Indian bird-stories one or two told in the Negro cabins of North Carolina, and probably elsewhere, and written down in Volume XI of the American *Folk-Lore Journal,* among many other tales of the out-door creatures to which the rural darkies like to attribute human attributes, and to use as puppets in their little comedies of animal life, which are likely to be keen satires on humanity. The one to be quoted is a parable of how Ann Nancy (a spider) got caught in a tight place by Mr. Turkey Buzzard, and how she escaped, for Mr. Buzzard was going to eat her.

"But," says the narrator, "she beg so hard, and compliment his fine presence, and compare how he sail in the clouds while she 'bliged to crawl in the dirt, till he that proudful and set up he feel mighty pardonin' spirit, and he let her go."

Ann Nancy, however, did not enjoy the incident, and "jess study constant how she gwine get the best of every creeter," and particularly of the tormenting bird.

"She knew Mr. Buzzard's weak point am he stomach, and one day she make it out dat she make a dining, and 'vite Mr. Buzzard an' Miss Buzzard an' de chillens. Ann Nancy she know how to set out a dinin' fo' sure, and when dey all got sot down to the table, an' she mighty busy passin' the hot coffee to Mr. Buzzard an' the little Buzzards, she have a powerful big pot o' scalding water ready, and she lip it all over poor ol' Mr. Buzzard's haid, and the po' ol' man done been baldhaided from that day.

"An' he don't forget on Ann Nancy, 'cause you 'serve she de onliest creeter on the topside the earth what Mr. Buzzard don't eat."

LIST OF BOOKS REFERRED TO

1. HALLIDAY, WILLIAM R. Greek Divination. (London, 1913.)
2. YOUNG, MARTHA. Plantation Bird Legends. (New York, 1902.)
3. WORCESTER, DEAN. The Philippines. (New York, 1901.)
4. BRINTON, DANIEL G. The Religions of Primitive Peoples. (New York, 1897.)
5. DORSEY, J. OWEN. Report U. S. Bureau of Ethnology, 1884-5. (Washington, 1888.)
6. McGEE, W. J. The Seri Indians, in Report U. S. Bureau Ethnology, 1895-6, Part I.
7. SKEAT, WILLIAM W. Malay Magic. (London, 1900.)
8. GAY, JOHN. Poems. The Shepherd's Week. (Boston, 1854.)
9. HIGGINSON, THOMAS W. Army Life in a Black Regiment. (Boston, 1870.)
10. SWANN, JAMES G. The Northwest Coast. (New York, 1857.)
11. FRIEND, HENRY. Flowers and Flower Lore. (London, 1883.)
12. SPENCE, LEWIS. Myths of the North American Indians. (London, 1914.)
13. DOUGHTY, CHARLES M. Wanderings in Arabia. (London, 1908.)
14. KEANE, JOHN F. T. Six Months in the Hejaz. (London, 1887.)
15. LAYARD, EDWARD L. The Birds of South Africa. (London, 1875-6.)
16. CANDLER, EDMUND. The Unveiling of Lhasa. (London, 1905.)
17. TYLOR, EDWARD B. Primitive Culture. (New York, 1920.)
18. KAY, CHARLES DE. Bird Gods of Ancient Europe. (New York, 1898.)
19. POWERS, STEPHEN. The Tribes of California. (Washington, 1877.)
20. MARTINENGO-CAESARESCO, COUNTESS E. L. The Place of Animals in Human Thought. (London, 1909.)
21. BARING-GOULD, SABINE. Curious Myths of the Middle Ages. (London, 1867.)
22. BROWN, ABBIE F. Book of Saints and Kindly Beasts. (Boston, 1900.) Consult also "Lives" of St. Francis of Assisi.

23. WARD, WILLIAM HAYES. Seal Wonders of Western Asia. (Carnegie Institution, No. 100.)
24. BAYLEY, HAROLD. The Lost Language of Symbolism. (London, 1913.)
25. DALTON, EDWARD T. Byzantine Art and Architecture.
26. Sacred Books of the East, Pahlavi Texts, Vol. XXIV, 112.
27. BRINTON, DANIEL G. Myths of the New World. (New York, 1868.) See also his American Hero Myths (1882).
28. OSWALD, FELIX. Zoological Sketches. (Philadelphia, 1883.)
29. ROTHERY, G. C. A B C of Heraldry. (Philadelphia, 1915.)
30. MALLET, PAUL H. Northern Antiquities. (London, 1890.)
31. GROSVENOR, EDWIN A. Constantinople. (Boston, 1895.)
32. GOLDSMITH, OLIVER. A History of the Earth and Animated Nature. (London, 1774.)
33. BROWNE, SIR THOMAS. Inquiry into Vulgar Errors. (London, 1846.)
34. BREWER, E. C. Handbooks, particularly "Phrase and Fable."
35. WALLACE, ALFRED RUSSEL. The Malay Archipelago. (New York, 1869.)
36. LEE, HENRY. Sea Fables Explained. (London, 1884.)
37. COOK, ARTHUR B. Zeus. (Cambridge, Eng., 1914.)
38. HULME, F. EDWARD. Natural History Lore and Legend. (London, 1895.)
39. WALKER, MARGARET C. Bird Legends and Life. (New York, 1908.)
40. WALTON, ISAAK. The Compleat Angler. (London, 100th Edition, 1888.)
41. ARISTOTLE. History of Animals. (London, Bohn, 1862.)
42. HARTING, J. E. The Ornithology of Shakespeare. (London, 1871). Compare Thiselton-Dyer's Folk Lore of Shakespeare.
43. HANAUER, J. E. Tales Told in Palestine. (Cincinnati, 1904.)
44. HUDSON, W. H. Birds of La Plata. (London, 1920.)
45. WHITE, GILBERT. Natural History of Selborne.
46. WILSON, ALEXANDER. North American Ornithology. (New York, 1853.)
47. SWANN, H. KIRKE. A Dictionary of English and Folk Names of British Birds. (London, 1913.) It contains a useful bibliography, and quotes largely from the Rev. C. Swainson's Folk Lore and Provincial Names of British Birds (English Dialect Society, 1886.)

48. St. Johnston, Lt.-Col. T. R. The Islanders of the Pacific. (London, 1921.)
49. Lyly, John. Euphues, or the Anatomy of Wit. (London, 1868.)
50. Coues, Elliott. Birds of the Northwest. (Washington, 1874.)
51. Cruden, Alexander. A Complete Concordance to the Holy Scriptures.
52. Laufer, Berthold. Bird Divination among the Thibetans. (Leiden, 1914.)
53. Miller, Leo. In the Wilds of South America. (New York, 1918.)
54. Gubernatis, Angelo de. Zoological Mythology. (New York, 1872.)
55. Newton, Alfred. Dictionary of Birds. (London, 1896.)
56. Conway, Moncure D. The Wandering Jew. (New York, 1881.) See also his Solomonic Literature (Chicago, 1899.)
57. Watters, John J. The Birds of Ireland. (Dublin, 1853.)
58. Sykes, Ella. Through Deserts and Oases of Central Asia. (London, 1914.)
59. Sale, George. The Koran (Alcoran of Mohammed.) (London, 1825.)
60. Wilde, Lady Jane F. Ancient Legends, Mystic Charms and Superstitions of Ireland. (London, 1902.)
61. Smith, Horatio. Festivals. (New York, 1836.)
62. Wentz, W. Y. The Fairy Faith in Celtic Countries. (London, 1911.)
63. Jenner, Mrs. Henry. Christian Symbolism. (London, 1910.)
64. O'Connor, Vincent C. Travels in the Pyrenees. (London, 1913.)
65. Bassett, Fletcher S. Legends and Superstitions of the Sea. (Chicago, 1888.)
66. Elworthy, F. T. The Evil Eye. (London, 1895.)
67. Gostling, Frances M. P. Rambles about the Riviera. (New York, 1914.) See also her books about the French chateaux, and the Bretons.
68. Ball, Mrs. Katherine M. Decorative Motives in Oriental Art. In *Japan* (magazine), New York, 1922.
69. Dryden, John. Ovid's Metamorphoses: "Transformation of Syrinx." (Boston, 1854.)
70. Bendire, Major Charles. Life Histories of North

American Birds, Vol. I. (Washington, Smithsonian Institution, 1892.)

71. MacBain, Alexander. Celtic Mythology and Religion. (Stirling, 1917.)

72. Frazer, Sir J. G. Golden Bough (series). The Scapegoat (1913).

73. Waterton, Charles. Essays (London, 1870). Also Wanderings in South America. (New York, 1910.)

74. Squire. Mythology of the British Isles. (London, 1905.)

75. Lanciani, Rodolph A. Pagan and Christian Rome. (Boston, 1893.)

76. Williams, Samuel W. The Middle Kingdom. (New York, 1883.)

77. Mooney, James. Report U. S. Bureau of Ethnology, Vol. XIV, 1892-3.

78. Broderip, W. J. Zoological Recreations. (London, 1849.)

79. Nuttall, Thomas. Manual of the Ornithology of the United States and Canada. (Cambridge, 1832.)

80. Heaton, Mrs. John L. By-Paths in Sicily. (New York, 1920.)

81. Irby, Col. Howard L. Ornithology of the Straits of Gibraltar. (London, 1875.)

82. Jones, W. Credulities Past and Present. (London, 1877.)

83. Swanton, John R. Report U. S. Bureau Ethnology, Vol. XXVI, 1904-5, p. 454.

84. Hazlitt, William C. Dictionary of Faiths and Folklore. (London, 1895.)

85. Stevenson, Hamilton S. Animal Life in Africa. (London, 1912.)

86. Manat, James I. Ægean Days. (London, 1913.)

87. The Arabian Nights: Payne's edition (London, 1901.)

88. Costello, Louis S. The Rose Garden of Persia. (London, 1899), including "Flowers and Birds" by Azz' Eddin Elmocadessi, "Jamshid's Courtship" by Firdausi, and prose notes.

89. Polo, Marco. Travels: Yule's edition. (London, 1875.)

90. Davis, F. H. Myths and Legends of Japan. (N. Y., 1912.) Consult also Joly, Henri L. Legend in Japanese Art. (London, 1908.)

91. Leland, Charles G. Kuloskap, the Master. (New York, 1902.)

92. Thiselton-Dyer, Thomas F. English Folklore. (Lon-

don, 1878.) Consult also his Folk-lore of Plants, and his Folk Lore of Shakespeare.

93. FIRDAUSI. The Shah Nameh: Atkinson's Translation. (London, 1886.)

94. PLUTARCH. Lives: Camillus, Romulus, Alexander, Etc.

95. Transactions of the Society of Biblical Archeology, Vol. viii, p. 80.

96. BOMBAUGH, C. C. Gleanings from the Harvest-Fields of Literature. (Baltimore, 1873.)

97. LELAND, CHARLES G. Etruscan Roman Remains in Popular Tradition. (London, 1892.)

98. FISKE, JOHN. Myths and Myth-Makers. (Boston, 1872.)

99. KEITH, GEORGE. Letters: in Les Bourgeis de la Compagnie du Nord-Ouest. (Quebec, 1889.)

100. NIBLACK, ALBERT P. Report U. S. National Museum, 1888.

101. NELSON, EDWARD W. Birds of Bering Sea and the Arctic Ocean. (Washington, 1883.)

102. SCHOOLCRAFT, HENRY G. Algic Researches. (New York, 1839.)

103. ADAMS, A. LEITH. Field and Forest Rambles. (London, 1873.)

104. MOONEY, JAMES. Report U. S. Bureau Ethnology, Vol. XIX, 1897-8, p. 401.

105. GRINNELL, GEORGE BIRD. Pawnee Hero–Stories and Folk-Tales. (New York, 1889.)

106. FORTIER, ALCE. Stories and Folk-Tales. (New York, 1889). Also, Louisiana Folk-Tales. (Boston, 1885.)

107. JAMESON, MRS. ANNA B. History of our Lord as Exemplified in Works of Art. (London, 1872). See also her Legends of the Monastic Orders (1872), and her Sacred and Legendary Art (1911).

108. VERRALL, MARGARET DE G. Mythology and Monuments of Ancient Athens. (London, 1890.)

109. DIODORUS SICULUS. Historical Library.

110. VILLARI, PASQUALE. The Barbarian Invasion of Italy. (New York, 1902.)

111. FOX-DAVIES, ARTHUR C. Complete Guide to Heraldry. (London, 1909.)

112. PERROT AND CHIPIEZ. History of Art in Antiquity: Vol. IV, Sardinia and Judea.

113. Seal of the United States: How it was Developed and Adopted. (Washington, Department of State, 1892.)

INDEX